PHILOSOPHY AND THE CONCEPTS
OF MODERN SCIENCE

THE MACMILLAN COMPANY
NEW YORK · BOSTON · CHICAGO · DALLAS
ATLANTA · SAN FRANCISCO

MACMILLAN & CO., LIMITED
LONDON · BOMBAY · CALCUTTA
MELBOURNE

THE MACMILLAN COMPANY
OF CANADA, LIMITED
TORONTO

PHILOSOPHY
AND THE CONCEPTS OF
MODERN SCIENCE

By

OLIVER L. REISER

*Associate Professor of Philosophy
in the University of Pittsburgh*

*

NEW YORK
THE MACMILLAN COMPANY
1935

PRINTED IN THE UNITED STATES OF AMERICA
BY THE STRATFORD PRESS, INC., NEW YORK

DEDICATED TO MY TEACHER

JOSEPH A. LEIGHTON

CONTENTS

INTRODUCTION

THAT the present age is one of critical examination in which scientific concepts, traditional institutions, and social practises are being weighed in the balance is an observation so trite that only purveyors of platitudes are guilty of calling attention to the fact. Nevertheless the reorganization in ideas and practises we are now undergoing is so fundamental that many tangled metaphors are invoked to describe this upheaval. One of the most curious manifestations of the sometimes paradoxical situation of modern culture is found in the fact that while science, in the course of the last several centuries, has progressively extended man's control over nature, it has at the same time been undermining its position as a theoretical discipline. Thus we find that after verifying Francis Bacon's dictum that knowledge is power, modern science is coming to see that power is not necessarily knowledge. As an example of this imbalance of theory and practise we need only point out that while science has increased its ability to predict and determine the future, there is as yet no adequate theory of "natural law" explaining and justifying these practical results. The status of induction, causality, probability, etc., is a scandal in the philosophy of science which is no whit abated by the advent of Heisenberg's famous "principle of indeterminacy."

Undoubtedly many thinkers, noting the fact that the crises in our economic-political systems parallel the need for theoretical reorientations in scientific structures, would regard this coincidence as purely accidental. But it is also possible to regard this necessity for readjustments in social relations and the theoretical foundations of science as two phases of the same unitary phenomenon. This, in fact, is the view of the situation taken by the *cultural interpretation* of history, a view which is reminiscent of the older organismic theory of society. In any case the fact remains that science today is being forced to criticize itself, its procedure and fundamental assumptions, to an extent never before even vaguely anticipated.

So thoroughgoing is this reconstruction that it reaches down into an examination of the logical tools we employ in all our thinking. In other words, one of the formulations now proposed as a necessary part of the new scientific methodology is that we develop a new logic to take the place of the older Aristotelian logic, which the human race has been employing for over two thousand years. Thus it is proposed that we adopt a non-Aristotelian logic, discarding the most fundamental laws of thought which have hitherto provided the regulatory principles according to which thinking has progressed. I have set forth my own reaction to this non-Aristotelian logic in Chapter III. My own view, which at the same time sets forth an alternative to the present popular movement of *Logical Positivism*, is expounded in Chapter V.

It is clear that in order to provide the new intellectual synthesis which the modern world must find, if it is not to disintegrate from lack of unifying principles and thus go down to destruction, it will be necessary for scientists to frame some unifying scheme which will be capable of integration with human culture and with human personality. The theoretical results of science must be humanized and the practical achievements of applied science must be socialized. But while we cry for interpreters, for scientific seers, who can lead us through the mazes of modern learning, our scientists for the most part remain philosophically inarticulate. In view of this situation in science those of us who regard it as the obligation of philosophy to attempt to coördinate the results of science may well ask ourselves, what is to be done?

In the following chapters I have set forth my own impressions of the nature and implications of the intellectual revolution which is in progress. The present view embodies several ideas which are current in present day thinking, namely, the method of phenomenology, the organic theory of nature, the theory of emergence, and the doctrine of humanism. These doctrines, which are somewhat distinct movements, I have tried to combine into one system. Let me indicate briefly the rôle which each of these ideas plays in the development of the present thesis. First let us glance at phenomenology.

As a possible method of integrating the vast and unwieldy masses of facts of the sciences into meaningful wholes the adoption of a phenomenological viewpoint is recommended. By phenomenology is meant a study of that which *exhibits* or *displays* itself: it is the *descriptive* point of view obtained by viewing a thing *as a whole*. Much of the trouble, it seems to me, comes from an overemphasis upon microscopic details. Thus it comes about that we can no longer see the forest for the trees. It is therefore proposed that we occasionally ascend in intellectual balloons and view the forest and ignore the trees! I do not know what term a Freudian would invoke to describe this "flight" from "reality," but it is interesting to note that scientists sometimes turn to this viewpoint. Those who have followed the recent developments in *gestalt* psychology have seen this method appear in psychology. An illustration of the phenomenological method may be found in the study of botany. We may view a flower as a phenomenal pattern, which is the attitude of *appreciation*. Or like the biochemist, who studies the intimate and complex mechanisms, we may analyze the petals of flowers into their intricate molecular structure. But we must never forget that the flower, in spite of its detailed complexity, possesses a *phenomenal simplicity* which is responsible for its *beauty* to us. Lest the reader fear that after all this is only poetry, let me recall that physics and chemistry, in employing the second law of thermodynamics, are also resorting to the phenomenal point of view. And this brings us to our own interpretation of the organic theory of nature as embodied in the doctrine of emergent evolution.

Several years ago, as pointed out in Chapter VII, the writer indicated that modern science is coming to recognize two types of "laws" in nature. This duality of natural law is stated in terms of a contrast between *dynamical* laws and *statistical* laws. The first type, *dynamical* laws, are *causal* laws, giving rigid determinism and predictability, and the second type, *statistical* laws, yield mere probability and introduce indeterminism into the calculations. A dynamical or causal law eliminates contingency, and implies ability to visualize the mechanisms in operation. But in statistical laws, concerned with the calculation of mean values, the individual elements of the statistical ensemble are not studied. Let us set down the contrasts between these two types of laws:

Dynamical Laws	*Statistical Laws*
1. *Illustrated by the principle of least action (including the first law of energetics).*	1. *Illustrated by the second law of energetics (or thermodynamics).*
2. *Causal (or necessary).*	2. *Probable (or contingent).*
3. *Microscopic processes are visualized.*	3. *Macroscopic states (or averaged results).*
4. *Real mechanisms.*	4. *Phenomenal viewpoint.*
5. *Reversible processes.*	5. *Irreversible processes.*

Here we see that the atomic processes of microscopic mechanisms are reversible (sometimes periodically) and subject to necessary causal laws, whereas the macroscopic states represent the mean value of a large number of individual processes of a statistical aggregate. It is sometimes supposed that since the mechanical processes are reversible, the second law of thermodynamics, expressing as it does the irreversible character of familiar natural processes, is necessarily a non-mechanical law. It must be noted, however, that the second law of thermodynamics does not contradict a dynamical law (such as the first law of energetics, more familiarly known as the principle of the conservation of energy), but is supplementary to it. The second law of thermodynamics (or energetics), which gives an *arrow* to time, as Eddington says, does not disturb the foundation of classical kinetic theory. Statistical mechanics, in fact, rests upon the conceptions of the mechanical-kinetic (microscopic) theory, *i.e.*, mass particles in motion. The real difference lies in point of view. The dualism between reversible and irreversible is associated with the dualism of the atomistic and the phenomenal points of view, as Max Planck observes in his book, *Survey of Physics* (p. 103).

The writer has on several occasions independently argued the thesis that it is the second law of thermodynamics which underlies the production of macroscopic or phenomenal states. It is interesting to note that Professor A. S. Eddington, in his work, *The Nature of the Physical World,* favors a dualism which parallels our own distinctions between *dynamical laws* and *statistical laws*. These are termed *primary* and *secondary* laws by Eddington (*op. cit.*, p. 75). According to Eddington, a primary law holds for the behavior of individuals and is indifferent to the time direction; whereas secondary laws hold for aggregates rather than individuals, express probable rather than necessary results, and therefore introduce "chance" into our picture of nature. Eddington states that it is the second law of thermodynamics, illustrating a secondary law, which gives to time the arrow which indicates direction or is responsible for irreversibility. This idea is entirely in harmony with the writer's supposition that the unidirectionality (irreversibility) of experienced time is a manifestation of the irreversibility of the biochemical reaction in the human brain, as these reactions proceed in accordance with the second law of thermodynamics. Some experimental verification for this view is provided by Professor Hudson Hoagland, in a paper to which he refers as he comments upon the present writer's view (cf. *Philosophy of Science*, Vol. I, 1934, 351).

While Professor Eddington accepts the second law of thermodynamics as an illustration of a secondary law, he does not explicitly regard it as the basis for the production of what, in the present view, is termed a macroscopic or phenomenal pattern. And yet our own interpretation here is quite in harmony with his view. Eddington tells us (*op. cit.*, pp. xiv-xv) that the external world has become a shadow world, and that the drama of familiar life, from the point of view of present day physics, is a shadowgraph performance. And now we ask, why should we not identify this "shadow world" with the phenomenological world of statistical ensembles which thereby *exhibit* themselves? Why shouldn't the second law of thermodynamics be generalized to provide the physical basis of macroscopic patterns, whether of molecular or of human societies? Eddington almost comes upon this view when he tells us (p. 105) that *entropy* is to be placed alongside *beauty* and *melody*, because they all three appear as features of *arrangement*. Thus nature produces what the writer has called *new simplicities,* or *second order simplicities,* out of *first order* or *simple simplicities.* This difference (except for the ultimate constituents of matter), is relative, *i.e.,* what is a simple simplicity from one point of view is a complex simplicity from another, just as a cell is an elementary unit in an organism (a unitary mode of behavior), but is also a complex aggregate of the large number of molecules of which it is constituted. Part of the present thesis is that the *gestalt* properties of the phenomenal macroscopic state are *field* properties.

In Part II of this work the idea that the second law of energetics is an expression of the tendency of statistical ensembles to come to some common basis of functional pattern is employed in a human social context. That is to say, just as consciousness is a macroscopic emergent from the activities of microscopic entities (neurone frequencies), so social patterns are phenomenological emergents from the social entities of statistical ensembles. This is our social philosophy of energetics. As indicated in the references, the attempt to employ the laws of energetics in a social *milieu* is not unprecedented, for Henry Adams, W. Ostwald, Edwin E. Slosson, and probably others, have made investigations along these lines. The advocates of "technocracy" have popularized the "energetic interpretation of history," but I find little that is new in their views.

And now how does humanism fit into this picture?

Of course there are various conceptions of the meaning of humanism. The implications of the term for ethics are pointed out in Chapter XV. In the field of the philosophy of science humanism is interpreted as a doctrine which stands midway between materialism and supernaturalism. Humanism as here understood holds that these are extreme views, and asserts that the truth lies in a compromise position which includes the best elements of both. Humanism is thus associated with the theory of emergent evolution. Humanism as a theory of nature becomes peculiarly interested in the drama of cosmic evolution at that point wherein man appears on the stage. Man today, in the rôle of the scientist, appears largely as a "student" of this wider world of nature from which the human race emerged. But man's eventual rôle may be quite different, in that he may become the "teacher" in that very cosmic classroom where first he learned to "obey" the laws of nature. Man cannot remain content to be a passive onlooker. His very growth in knowledge and in wisdom will undoubtedly make a difference to the future direction of nature's course. Humanism adopts the position that the final fate of our cosmos cannot be calculated without taking into account the rôle which humanity is to play in the subsequent acts of this as yet incomplete, and perhaps forever unending, drama. And so the naturalist and the humanist join in with the ancient voice of hope and triumph: It doth not yet appear what man shall be!

And now a few words concerning those persons who have influenced me most in the development of my own thoughts. Of course my former teachers have had much to do with the shaping of my views. Here I refer especially to Professors J. A. Leighton, A. P. Weiss, A. R. Chandler, A. E. Avey, B. H. Bode, and H. H. Goddard. From my present colleagues, Professors M. R. Gabbert and Richard Hope, I have received stimulus and helpful criticism. In addition to these influences, and over a period of years, I have been the recipient of counsel and suggestions from others who have been interested in my mental evolution. Among those who, at one time or an-

other, have passed judgment on my work are Doctors
Christine Ladd-Franklin, Marvin Farber, G. P. Conger,
D. L. Evans, Harry Helson, Hudson Hoagland, N.
Rashevsky, Edwin E. Slosson, Smith Ely Jelliffe, G. E.
Coghill, W. M. Malisoff, Herbert Feigl, Charles Hartshorne, A. J. Lotka, Archibald Henderson, M. Lukiesh,
and Count Alfred Korzybski. I wish to thank these
persons for their comments and criticisms, destructive
as well as constructive, even though I have not always
benefited from their suggestions to the extent that they
intended. Finally I wish to thank my wife for her unfail-
ing patience and encouragement during the period of the
writing of this book.

Chapter IX of the book is a revised version of an article
on "The Biological Origins of Religion," which first appeared in the *Psychoanalytic Review,* January, 1932
(Vol. 19). I am indebted to the Editor of this review for
permission to use that article here. Part of the last chapter is taken from a paper on "The Social Objectives of
Humanism," which was first read before the First Humanist Assembly in New York City on October 11, 1934.
These meetings were organized by Dr. Charles Francis
Potter. Professor John Dewey was kind enough to take
part in this symposium. My own paper was published in
the *New Humanist,* December, 1934, and is here reproduced by permission of the journal. Aside from an occa-
sional quotation, the remainder of the material of this
volume has not previously appeared in print in this
country.

O. L. R.

PART I

PHILOSOPHY AND THE PHYSICAL SCIENCES

CHAPTER I

IDEALISM AND SCIENTIFIC REALITY

I. Science and Human Progress

AGES, like human beings, have their fashions. Like the men that live in them, periods of history have their individual modes of expression. And so we moderns, not to be outdone, must also have our cultural eccentricities. And who can deny that we have? Is it not obvious that one of the peculiar idiosyncrasies of the modern era is the belief in progress? Even the Great War and the Depression have not permanently damaged our optimistic faith in the future.

There are other intellectual modes which characterize the present age, but let us pause for a moment and examine more closely this confidence we have that history is not purposeless. Progress, as we all know, implies direction in time. The idea carries with it the implication that the past was a preparation for the present, which in turn can be succeeded by an even more perfect future. Accordingly, under the influence of this idea, we have come to regard the course of history from the Ape-man (or the Dawn-man) to the modern period as the record of the increasing realization of civilization. In our charitable moments our enlightened futurists of culture will grant that the Middle Ages constituted but an intermission in the drama of cultural progress, a detour on the somewhat winding but ever ascending highway to the

3

modern world. Like the barbarism of early savagery,
Mediævalism was a resting place along the road to the
New World of modern culture. Now we are going forward
again.

And so we moderns try to understand ourselves in the
light of what man has been. With the passion of cru-
saders we explore the historical and psychological influences which enter into the structure of human nature
and social institutions. The results of such studies, we
are convinced, not only show us how we have come to
be what we are, but also help us in the process of controlling social evolution. Therefore we write books on
the "modern mind" and how it is made and is still in the
"making." An old sage once remarked that of the writing
of books there is no end. If he were alive today he would
say that of the writing of books on the making of the
modern mind there is no end. But instead of finding these
books a weariness to the flesh, our erstwhile cynic would
now probably read them with avidity.

Behind all this social diagnosis and political psycho-
analysis lies a serious purpose. The impetus behind our
introspection concerning our cultural hinterland is the
belief that this knowledge will give us a mastery over
the future. Knowledge is power, we echo with Francis
Bacon, the founder of modernism. We look forward to
the time when man will consciously control the "direction
of human evolution." Our potentialities are limitless, we
like to believe.

At the present time it is fashionable to enumerate the
various "movements" which have served to bring about
the present world. The contemporary philosophical historian asks the question: What forces have done most to
undermine the previous culture of Western Europe, thus
introducing the new civilization? In answer to this the

cultural historian [1] sets down the following movements as being the most important in the creation of the modern world:

1. The Renaissance
2. The Reformation
3. The Development of Modern Science
4. The Growth of Nationalism and Democracy
5. The Doctrine of Natural Rights
6. The Industrial Revolution

Our philosophical historian then discusses each of these movements, bringing to bear much scholarly research in evaluating the importance of each force. He summarizes his learned analysis by pointing out that the modern world is more a result of the practical applications of scientific research than it is of any other factor. He will marshal up much evidence in support of this view. He will show how the whole economic, financial, and industrial organization of society developed along side the machine. The inventor of the steam engine and the discoverer of the laws of electromagnetism, he tells us, have done more to revolutionize the old world and to create the new environment than all the exhortations of philosophers and of priests. He will point out how nationalism and democracy have also received their impetus from the applications of science and discovery. Thus our historian continues to pile up confirmatory evidence. By way of putting the capstone on the argument he concludes by showing how the invention of the printing press, making knowledge (and also the Bible) accessible to all, undermined the ecclesiastical monopoly on learning, and how this finally broke the domination of the Church.

This story of the growth of science is indeed inspiring and might well be taken as an earnest of the power of

[1] Cf. J. A. Leighton's text, *The Field of Philosophy*, 1930, Chapter 13.

that creative intelligence which is to build the new universe for us. The optimism to which science gives rise follows from a line of reasoning which is briefly stated and easy to understand: We first note what remarkable changes have been introduced by discoveries in physics and chemistry. We then point out the obvious fact that we have hardly made a beginning in the application of scientific methods to social problems. We observe that the sciences of medicine, biology, psychology and sociology are still in their infancy, and that their progress may be as rapid and fruitful as that of their sister sciences working in the field of the inorganic. Hence we conclude that as soon as we learn how to apply the knowledge which biology and the social sciences are now beginning to put at our disposal the result will be equally astounding and satisfactory. In that day, as J. B. S. Haldane points out in his *Daedalus,* we will create human nature according to the demands of social engineers, who will solve the problems of society by dealing with the human beings of the political organization as the chemist now works with the molecules. This line of reasoning naturally forces upon us the necessity for "humanizing" knowledge, so that by intelligent social coöperation we can hasten the day. Our responsibility is to teach the new "decalogue of science" which is to usher in the utopia. It is a race between education and catastrophe, we are told, and science alone can give us the knowledge and the power to avert social disaster. Science is the Moses to lead us into the Promised Land.

II. The Menace of Science

The foregoing paragraphs give us in brief form the essence of a widely prevailing set of intellectual fashions.

In stating these modes and manners of the progressive mind of today we are neither approving nor ridiculing them. It may be that this attitude is entirely wholesome and has every pragmatic sanction which it needs. It may very well be that, as one prominent philosophical physicist has asserted, the notion of progress is the most important which the human mind has developed. But not all who have studied this problem of the effects, immediate and remote, of science upon human life can accept this favorable interpretation. Not only are they dissatisfied with the picture I have painted of the contemporary mind, but they are also unconvinced of the validity of the optimistic conclusions which our philosophical historian has drawn.

Of course we always have with us the knocker and the pessimist. He is the disillusioned cynic whose joy in life (perhaps also his bankroll) comes from mocking all serious attempts at reforming the world. In the eyes of such a person optimistic enthusiasms, whether engendered by science, religion or ethics, represent a kind of juvenile exuberance, and since each new age appears in its youth, human beings will always be looking forward to a future which is rosier than the present. These wise men will tell us that the only thing which history teaches us is that history teaches us nothing—if it did we would know that human beings are always expecting the coming of new saviors of mankind. The latest of these false messiahs whom human beings are worshipping happens to be Science.

But after all, such scoffers at everything are in the minority, and their somewhat flippant and facetious views do not represent the opinions of any important or numerous group of persons who seriously question whether the dominance of science and scientific method in modern times is on the whole beneficial. There are, however, other groups of intelligent persons who have honestly come to the conclusion that scientific advance may prove a curse rather than a blessing to the human race.

We are all familiar with the prevalent argument that the World War, which threatened seriously to destroy what we Occidentals regard as the finest civilization of the earth, was but an expression of the fact that scientific progress had outstripped our moral and spiritual progress. According to those who hold this view, our ability to release the forces of nature outran our ability to use the power which thus came with scientific knowledge for the permanent benefit of the whole human race. If our philosophical historian had been sufficiently keen of vision to see the low lights as well as the high lights of the picture he would have discerned in the background the evils which follow in the footsteps of advancing science. He would have noted that nationalism flourishes in unified countries; that it is the result of the creation of a group consciousness in the people of the state, and that science, in giving us rapid transit, autos, newspapers, telephones, and similar mechanisms, has facilitated the development of mass feelings. And since wars are frequently the expression of the natural fears and prejudices which are nourished by nationalism, science has contributed directly to the tendency towards wars. Moreover, along with the advance in machine production there always develops the need for finding new markets, and thus applied science fosters imperialistic policies and tends to cause more national competition.

In reply to this disparagement of science our advocate of more science might reply that science is itself international in character, that it flourishes most in times of peace, and that it calls for human coöperation rather than human destruction. But as Bertrand Russell has pointed out in his book, *Icarus*, it is an unfortunate fact that scientists, as citizens of their respective states, are always under the thumbs of the politicians, who use the results of science for their own selfish ends. And thus the results of science are prostituted on the markets of commercialism. But in reply to this the scientist will probably point out that all we need to do to abolish the prostitution of science is to change the character (or "reaction patterns") of the people of which society is constituted. The use of the results of pure research for selfish purposes means that we need more social science; we need a science of human behavior telling us how to produce the type of individuals we wish, and how to eliminate the undesirable types. Our ethics must work hand in hand with biology, we are told.

That something of this sort is actually taking place is readily seen. Science is actually making inroads upon domains formerly held by religion and ethics. The medical man and the psychiatrist are encroaching more and more upon the fields of human conduct which formerly were the undisputed provinces of priests. A few decades ago, when a calamity or an epidemic overtook a community, the people rushed to the church and prayed to the Lord for forgiveness of their sins; now, in the case of a disease which is of an infectious nature, the churches to which the people formerly hastened may be closed. Thus, in one way or another, the doctor and the mental hygiene expert are taking over the duties monopolized in earlier ages by spiritual advisors.

Various motives, not always unselfish, have been behind the opposition to science. In the case of the conflict between the scientific and the religious groups there is sometimes reason to suspect that this fear concerning the effects of science arises out of the jealousy of a rival which threatens eventually to dispose of all competition. But in many cases this uneasiness with which individuals view the progress of science has as its basis no such selfish motives. The loss of faith in the actuality and efficacy of spiritual realities, which seems to accompany the spread of the scientific attitude, is a tragedy not only in the eyes of the defenders of religious creeds. Leaders in ethical thought, who presumably have no spiritual axes to grind, have also sometimes wondered whether the alleged increase in crime and immorality may not be due, at least in part, to the decline of the idealistic view-point—a decline which is the inevitable result of the ascendancy of the mechanistic viewpoint of science. With increasing boldness science has extended its methods and concepts, until it is now attacking that last citadel of idealism—man himself. Human conduct is treated by the mechanistic behaviorist as on a par with the behavior of the lower animals. Is this, then, what the scientific attitude means? Is this the scientific method we wish to see established? If the scientific point of view means mechanism, then there are not a few who will join with religious leaders in the hope that science will not monopolize and dominate human thought and action.

Another group believing that there is a clash between the interests of their particular field and the attitude of science is the poets. The apparently inescapable hostility between the scientific and the poetic viewpoints has frequently been noted. Those of us who would like to see both pursuits continue to flourish are pondering how the appreciative attitude of the poet and the artist is to be harmonized with the cold intellectualism and heartless analysis which is supposed to be present in the scientific method. The basis of this conflict has been pointed out by Mr. I. A. Richards in his little volume on *Science and Poetry*. Even John Dewey, who seldom gets excited about anything, tells us: "There is no more significant question before the world than this question of the possibility and method of reconciling the attitudes of practical science and contemplative æsthetic experience."

Before we attempt to discover how these widening breaches between science, religion, and art are to be bridged, it is necessary to have clearly articulated in consciousness the precise sources of these seeming incompatibilities.

III. ANTHROPOMORPHISM IN POETRY AND RELIGION

It is my belief that when we understand why there is a conflict between science and religion we will also understand why there is a hostility between science and poetry. This statement implies that religion and poetry, insofar as they stand in opposition to science, have something in common. In putting forth this view I am fully aware that there are followers of the arts who disclaim any connection, sympathy or common cause whatsoever between art and religion. In reply it may be pointed out that while it is true that poetry does not necessarily involve any sort of theistic ideas, and to that extent is quite independent of religion or morality, in other respects, principally in connection with the need for finding or creating stimuli in our environment to give expression to the emotional nature within us, religion and poetry do have much in common. That is to say, art and religion, psychologically viewed, have similar functions. Freudian psychology regards religion and art as types of *compensation thinking,* a kind of activity in which we make up for the shortcomings of the real world studied by science in its *reality thinking*. In art we create an ideal world where in imaginative embodiments we rise above the limitations of a drab and picayune environment. It goes without saying that poets and religionists are not likely to look with favor upon any theory which denies reality to the objects of æsthetic experience; but that raises another question which it is not necessary to discuss at the present time. All that I am now insisting upon is that religion and art are *expansive* in their effects; they provide releases for our emotions, whereas science demands a drawing in of our feelings. Science calls for a *contraction* of that tendency which in religion and art is outward-flowing.

The essence of the matter seems to me to lie in this: Both religion and art represent a more natural, a more naïve, point of view than is embodied in science. Science arises out of a somewhat artificial attitude—artificial in the sense that it is the product of a severe and austere discipline. Poetry and religion are an expression of the primitive and child-like, in the sense that they give release to the emotional insurgence which suffuses the world with a penumbra of affective coloring which has the effect of transfiguring the objects of æsthetic perception.

In making these statements we are not unmindful of the actual differences which exist between religion and poetry (or art in general). Nor do we mean to say that there is *no* intellectual element present in religion and art. Who would deny the intellectual titanism of a Leonardo da Vinci, a Beethoven, a Shakespeare? Nor is it true that there are *no* emotional satisfactions present in scientific investigation and discovery. We have only to think of the effect of the discovery of the laws of planetary motion on Kepler, or the way in which Newton was overwhelmed by the discovery of the law of gravitation, to see the falsity of such a view. What I am saying is that in the main it is true that science, as it has been interpreted in the past and as it is now generally understood, has little room for the emotional elements which predominate in the religious or artistic experiences. It is universally agreed that to the extent that a scientist's judgments are influenced by emotional factors to that extent his conclusions are unreliable. Science, in its search for facts, demands freedom from affective inclinations. This presumably is what is meant by the term the "objectivity" of science.

This leads us to another distinction between the scientific attitude and the religio-æsthetic attitude. The person whose child-like attitude towards his environment has not been warped by scientific studies is a naïve realist: he believes that the qualities we perceive are actually *in* nature—the colorful beauty of sunset is "out there" in the environment, and not in us. But science, treating the world it studies as a series of concatenated mechanisms, devoid of all those subjective elements which we read into the processes and forms of nature, tells us that there is no color in nature: there are only waves of light undergoing unequal refractions, selective absorptions, etc., as they make their passage through the dust particles of the air. The red of the rose, we are told, is not in the rose, but in us. Therefore when you go to the florist to buy the lady of your heart some red roses what you should really ask for—if you are going to be scientific— is this: I want a dozen of roses having that type of chemical composition so that the "red" rays of the visible spectrum are reflected and all other wave lengths are absorbed! The psychologist tells us that it is this tendency to read our conscious experiences into the objective world which gives rise to illusions, delusions, and hallucinations. Against this reduction of the colorful artistry of nature to the status of hallucinations poetry and religion protest. They protest because the tendency to dehumanize nature into meaningless and purposeless juxtapositions of mass particles in space leaves nothing in nature to provide the stimuli whose function is to release our emotional energies. To prove this point it will be necessary to show that the appeal of the objects of the religious and the artistic experiences arises out of the less sophisticated view of nature which is termed *animism*.

Anyone who will take the trouble to analyze the composition which gives him an æsthetic thrill will find that the "kick" results from the humanization of the objects and processes which elicit this reaction. This tendency to spill over our feelings into the environment about us, to bring even the inanimate world closer about us by endowing all forms and utterances of nature with a soul, is designated technically by the term "anthropomorphism." But this animistic tendency to treat inanimate things as possessing a vital spirit or a personal power is not restricted to primitive man, in whom this attitude toward nature originated. The individual who treats an unruly automobile, or an innocent hammer which unwittingly lands on his thumb, as possessed of a personal force is reacting to a thing as though it were a person with malicious purposes. Now we here contend that in all religioæsthetic experiences we are doing the same thing which the previously mentioned individual is doing when, in a fit of anger, he treats an object as though it were a person and accordingly tells it what he thinks of it. The principal difference lies in the fact that the artist creates situations which more frequently appeal to pleasing emotions than to anger or fear. The æsthetic response usually calls into play the sense of beauty. A few illustrations will suffice to show that the artistic experience arises out of the tendency to break down the barriers between the subjective and the objective.

In describing the interior of a Scottish castle Sir Walter Scott speaks of the "slumbering sword" which is suspended on the wall. This expression has its appeal because it brings this object within the range of familiar experiences; this figure of speech suggests a sleeping child, temporarily inactive, which has indulged in much action in the past, and is capable of indulging in more activity in the future. Another illustration of that anthropomorphic element in poetry which allows us to project into nature our own feelings is presented in the statement of the poet who said, "the mountain lifted up its shoulder." If a scientist were to state the height of a mountain he would say that its top was so many feet (or meters) above sea level. A poet would probably regard such a statement as stale, flat, and prosaic. The poet's expression conveys the impression of an Atlas straining upwards into the heavens, trying to hold aloft the sky. Clearly this involves a personification. Such expressions bring an otherwise indifferent and alien environment into a kind of rapport with ourselves. This is reminiscent of primitive tribes of men who saw spirits of good and evil pervading the forces and objects of nature. For the modern poet as well as for the primitive philosopher the wind, running streams, the clouds, and the storm are ensouled. The following quotation, in which Baudelaire, the French poet, is giving us a description of the psychological effects of the use of hashish, seems to me to present an excellent summary of the tendency which is also to be associated with the æsthetic experience:

It often happens that personality disappears and that objectivity, which is the property of Pantheistic Poets, develops so abnormally that the contemplation of objects outside yourself makes you forget your own existence, and causes you to lose yourself in them. Suppose you look at a tree, gracefully waving in the wind; in a few seconds, what in the brain of a poet was no more than a natural comparison, becomes a reality in yours. First you attribute to the tree your passions, your desire or your melancholy; its murmurs and its writhings become yours, and before long you are the tree. In the same way, the bird that flies to the outermost regions of the skies represents the first immortal desire to fly above things human; but already you are yourself the bird.

It seems entirely plausible that this state, which Baudelaire pictures as *Les Paradis Artificiels* of drug addicts, is induced in the poet without artificial stimulation. In art you lose yourself in the contemplations of objects with which you identify your being.

Humanizing nature is attributing to it all the tingling warmth, the variegated color, the zestful, melancholy, or angry feeling which the learned psychologists now tell us is in ourselves and not in the external world. That the projection of the subjective emotions of the artist into the external world is an important element in the appreciative attitude is recognized by that psychological theory of art which explains æsthetic perception in terms of "empathy" or *einfühlung*. This empathic element is always present in a poetic interpretation of nature. On the other hand, the objective scientist attempts to keep his emotions and humanizations in the background. He refuses to see spirits behind the manifestations of nature. He sees only a depersonalized cosmos of insensate matter rolling on its indifferent way, sublimely unconscious of man's hopes, fears, loves, and aspirations. To the poetic and religious mind it seems that science has stripped nature of her rich garments; with X-ray analysis science sees through the warm personality of nature only the skeletal outlines of a ghostly world of masses in motion. Nature is no longer dressed up, and therefore she is not going anywhere.

This brings us to another point where the shoe of science pinches the toes of anthropomorphism. Not only does science make subjective, and therefore ephemeral if not unreal, those qualities which common sense, and poetry, and religion put into nature, but in dehumanizing and depersonalizing the events of nature science removes the possibility of an interpretation in which we can believe there is some end or purpose behind or in the processes of nature. If nature is to have some goal or purpose, nature in some respects resembles human nature. That a belief in the purposive interpretation of the drama of cosmic processes is an essential element of the religious view will be readily accepted. That the same belief in the controlling intelligence giving meaning to nature is also an essential element of poetry is not so obvious, and therefore stands in need of justification. To this we now turn.

IV. POETRY VERSUS MECHANISM

It is the burden and the mystery of this unintelligible world which drives all human beings to echo the cry of Shelley:

Whence are we and why are we? Of what scene
The actors or spectators?

It may be that this is the question to which there is no answer; it may be that the problem of the whenceness of the isness of things will forever remain an inscrutable riddle of the sphinx. Nevertheless, we are compelled by our natures to try to find the answer. And, in effect, it seems clear that science and poetry, each in its own way, has already suggested an answer. Of course, it is probable that these answers are not final, and that the future will see old problems answered in new ways. But I think that it is possible to contrast the types of solutions presented at the present time by these two attitudes.

The contrast seems to me to lie in this: Poetry and religion favor an *idealistic* view of nature; science, on the other hand, favors a *mechanistic* explanation of nature. These terms are vague. So the contrast may be stated in another way by noting that idealism tends to regard the meaning of nature as being given in terms of the highest things which nature has produced. That is to say, poetic and religious idealism read nature's meaning *forward;* they interpret nature in terms of her highest products. Here on earth, man, with his intelligence and emotions, gives us the best clue to the interpretation of the cosmos as a whole. And science? Let me quote the following verse and ask you whether this is the utterance of a poet or a scientist?

> Every clod feels the stir of might
> An instinct within that reaches and towers;
> And grasping blindly above it for light,
> Climbs to a soul in grass and flowers.

Surely we can all agree that this is not science! Science tends to read nature's meaning *backward*. The scientific interpretation of nature consists in understanding the laws of the eternal elements out of which all things are constructed. Not in the latest products of nature, but in the ultra-microscopic mechanisms within the atoms, lies the clue to the interpretation of nature's secrets. This view is well stated in the following passage from John Tyndall's famous Belfast Address:

Abandoning all disguises, the confession I feel bound to make before you is that I prolong the vision backward across the boundary of the experimental evidence, and discern in that which we, in our ignorance and notwithstanding our professed reverence for its creator, have hitherto covered with opprobrium the promise and potency of every form and quality of life.

The essence of idealism is to be found in the belief that we are living in a universe in which our emotional values are something more than inexplicable exudations from ductless glands. Dynamic idealism is the protest against the view that cosmic processes are *meaningless*. In order to believe that nature as a whole has meaning it is necessary to believe that the processes of nature have direction. This means that there must be instinct in the processes of nature something analogous to that which we apprehended in our experience of conscious duration as progress in time. To hold such a view the idealist *must* anthropomorphize nature. If materialism were true then all that could happen would be the recombinations into different configurations of the ultimate particles of matter. But since time would not count in such a system one permutation or combination of elements would be as significant as any other. In such a system, as Bergson has pointed out, *nothing new can happen.* For this reason idealism has always appealed to those individuals in whom the wish is father to the thought. The emotional satisfactions of an idealistic interpretation are brought out in the well-known lines of Pope's *Essay On Man:*

> All are parts of one stupendous whole
> Whose body Nature is, and God the Soul.

It is true that not all poets have reacted in the same way to science. Some poets might see in materialism much to inspire the fine frenzy of creative effort. Lucretius, for example, seemed to attack with enthusiasm the problem of the poetic dramatization of the earlier Greek atomism of Leucippus and Democritus. It may also be true that not all artistic temperaments believe that "all charms fly at the touch of cold philosophy." But on the whole the tendency has been to regard science as the surgical scissors which would "clip the wings of the angels." In such a view the lines which Wordsworth applied to the philosopher might with equal appropriateness be applied to the scientific interpreter:

> A fingering slave
> One that would peep and botanize
> Upon his mother's grave.

Science ridicules the "vision splendid" and the "trailing clouds of glory" which inform the poet of another reality than the world of sense. In the lines composed above Tintern Abbey this feeling of kinship with a deeper reality within nature than is grasped through scientific analysis appears in its most exalted form:

> And I have felt
> A presence that disturbs me with the joy
> Of elevated thought; a sense sublime
> Of something far more deeply interfused,

Whose dwelling is the light of setting suns,
And the round ocean and the living air,
And the blue sky, and in the mind of man;
A motion and a spirit, that impels
All thinking things, all objects of all thought,
And rolls through all things.

Undoubtedly this is good poetry, but to the materialistic psychologist the "motion and spirit which roll through all things" would be recorded as a series of waves on the smoked drum of a kymograph. According to John B. Watson such beauty of expression is only a series of laryngeal contractions.

It is only by a heroic effort that the poet Tennyson, struggling with the Darwinian picture of nature "red in tooth and claw," gathers together the disintegrating bits of a threatened intellectual chaos and affirms his faith in "one increasing purpose" running through the ages. In his *In Memoriam* he has the vision of

One God, one law, one element
And one far-off divine event
To which the whole creation moves.

But Tennyson lived before Einstein, who now tells us that time measurements are relative, and that therefore there can be no absolute standard which enables us to assert progress toward one far-off divine event. No wonder, then, that the relativists should feel constrained to revise Tennyson's version and assert, in the words of Bertrand Russell:

The one far-off divine event
Toward which some things move,
And away from which other things move.

It is one of the curious paradoxes of modern thought that science, which has done so much to justify our belief in intellectual progress, should itself develop within its own province the notion which is to undermine the idea of progress. Perhaps the reader fears that he will now have to wade through another "popularization" of the theory of relativity. Fortunately he will have to do no such thing. I shall assume that every high grade organism (to use one of Dr. A. N. Whitehead's exquisite terms) is familiar with the more important and less difficult notions in the theory of relativity.

V. Anthropomorphic Mechanics and Relativity

Aside from the matter which we have just discussed, there is another respect in which relativity undermines the anthropomorphism of religion and poetry. If the theory of relativity is true the notion of *force*, conceived as the *cause* of the motions and activities of matter, must be abandoned.

Up to the present even physics has not been entirely successful in its attempt at banishing animistic and vitalistic survivals from its domain. It is quite generally agreed that the notion of "force" developed out of the sense of effort which we experience when we put bodies into motion by overcoming their "inertia." By analogy to this experience of effort it was argued that the forces of nature must be the active producers of the changes which occur, and that these forces actually overcome resistances. The old argument as to what would happen if an irresistible force met with an immovable object has meaning only when we grant this interpretation of force as the power which overcomes the inertia of matter. This objectification of the sense of effort resulted in what Henri Poincaré has termed "anthropomorphic mechanics." While most physicists now recognize that "force" is not an actual entity or agency, but only a name describing an important change of relationship between bodies, nevertheless there did linger along something of the more primitive animistic view of a force of nature as the expression of a spirit within, having emotionally initiated purposes to accomplish. Schopenhauer openly embraced this view when he argued that everything in nature is a crystallization of will. Even such a materialistically minded scientist as Haeckel thinks of the force of chemical affinity in an animistic fashion as the expression of affection between atoms and molecules.

When Newton formulated his famous law that bodies attract each other directly as their masses and inversely as the square of the distance he framed no hypothesis to explain this "attraction." But most of us think of the "force" of gravity as something which actually "draws" the objects together. This is a highly satisfying explanation to those who are too lazy or too busy to look for a better one. Unfortunately, this comfortable view must now be abandoned—at least so Einstein informs us. Relativity has sounded the death knell of animistic physics, we are told. The reason for this can readily be shown, and without the use of any complicated mathematics.

The familiar equation for force, as every high school pupil glibly recites it, is this: *Force = Mass × Acceleration*. It will be noted that in this equation there is an acceleration, which is a velocity squared. This refers to the fact that a body is held to be acted upon by a force when it is undergoing a change of rate of motion. This is well known in the case of a falling object which is obeying the force of gravity. This interpretation of force in all probability originated in the observation that in order to change the state of a body we must exert a push or pull. If there were no resistance (*i.e.*, if we had a machine with frictionless bearings), once the object or machine was set in motion it would continue in motion indefinitely, as Newton's first law of motion tells us. Hence a force is said to be that which tends to change the state of a body, whether it be at rest or in motion. It is at this point that Einstein enters upon the scene and "dephlogisticates" this notion of force as a cause. When we calculate the motion of a body we say that it is in motion or at rest with respect to some other body which we take to be at rest. For our human practical purposes the earth is the most important body in the universe, and like the people of the days gone by we think of motions referred to the earth as the center of reference. We say that a train is stationary, or in motion, because, in our geocentric theory, the earth is our fixed "frame of reference." But if we free ourselves from the bias which practical considerations have forced upon our minds we see that we have no right to assume that the earth is absolutely at rest. We know, for example, that the earth is revolving in its orbit about the sun, that the sun and our whole solar system is moving off into space toward a certain constellation, and that someday we may collide with something else—which may be the end of us, but not of the relativity of motion. When we are dealing with rectilinear motions we can assert that any body is in motion only if we assume that some other body is at rest. But this body with reference to which we are measuring the first body may itself be in motion with respect to some other body, and so on. Unless we can find some body which is absolutely stationary we can never say with certainty whether any particular body is "really" in motion or is at rest. The older theories assume that the ether of space constituted such an absolutely fixed frame of reference. But as every one knows, some—if not all—experiments indicate that the ether behaves as if it did not exist. Such modesty is so unusual that it is certainly too bad that Einstein cannot reward the ether with something better than the ungracious proposal to ignore its existence. If, then, there are no absolutely fixed frames of reference in nature we cannot really say whether any object is really at rest, in uniform motion, or whether it is undergoing positive or negative acceleration of motion. And since the test of whether a body is being acted upon by a force is the test of accelerated motion, we must conclude that force, like motion, is relative. Both force and motion were formerly supposed to refer to objective facts of nature only because we introduced anthropomorphism and geocentrism into nature. Now we recognize that this anthropocentric interpretation of the external world no longer affords us the criteria necessary to support a view which originated in the philosophy of primitive man. Hence the new physics is chanting the funeral march of anthropomorphic mechanics. Another fossil of the human mind has gone to its resting place.

Not only does relativity strike at the roots of the animistic interpretation of the external world; it may also be applied to the world of inner experience, to man's own sense of active causation. Let us consider the case of a man who strikes another man in a fit of anger. All this means in relativity physics is that the world-line of the fist of the aggressor intersects the world-line of the nose of the man who is struck. Physiological relativity would ask us to believe that the angry state of consciousness, which common sense tells us was the real cause of the subsequent impact, was not the force which produced the

crossing of the geodesics, but that the space-time between the objects was so modified (crinkled, distorted,
humped, or what-not) that the fist of the pugnacious
man merely tobogganed down an incline, taking the
shortest path in the four-dimensional manifold. (This is
Bertrand Russell's illustration, I believe.) This view that
consciousness has no causal efficacy in producing bodily
movements was first set forth in the now famous James-
Lange theory of the emotions. If we accept the above
explanation as a valid description of the way in which
the hummock in space-time which we call a man's nose
comes to expand itself under the influence of the infinitely near approach of another hummock which we
call a fist, then James's theory receives a curious verification which James himself never anticipated.

VI. The Refutation of Materialism

Here we have modern physics and psychology arrayed
against the ancient forces of animism and anthropomorphism. In dehumanizing nature and human nature science seems to take away the incentive to productivity in
many fields of human enterprise. If the future is already
mapped out, if the notion of a creative process in time
is an illusion, then the notion we have that we are
real agents in the making of history is false. If the stratification by our consciousness of the universe into a
unique time-dimension is illusory, if three-dimensional
dynamics is to be absorbed into the *statics* of a four-fold
realm of space-time, where the distinction between past,
present, and future is lost, then indeed our consciousness
of progress in time is a profound paradox. If it follows
from the statement that there is no difference between
space and time—except that time as the fourth coördinate

of space requires a minus sign in the geometry of modern physics—then our faith that man in some measure can control his own destiny and the fate of social evolution is a delusion. If the seemingly intuitive flow of conscious time and of growth is nothing more than the result of an arbitrary stratification of nature, then surely the feeling of spontaneity within us is a snare. If the sense of the mastery of the vicissitudes of life is such a delusion then why labor to create a better social order? If whatever is to be already is then why travail to better international understanding and avert another war? These are some questions which some persons would like to ask. The reply would probably be that relativity is a physical doctrine, and as such has nothing to do with psychological or social facts. But is this true? Certainly it cannot be true in any form of materialism, where "psychic" processes are only special illustrations of physical processes and laws. But no matter what our psychological theory may be, we know that the movements which our bodies execute are constantly intersecting the physical world in which and upon which we act. Moreover, if a man's thoughts *are* the electrochemical reactions in the cortex —or the muscular contractions in the larynx, à la Watson—then how does the actual irreversible experience of conscious duration arise out of the interactions of brain molecules where past, present, and future swallow each other up?

Let us summarize these ideas in the following dilemma: either (*a*) man's responses are only special applications of the laws of physics, or (*b*) the laws of physics are not pertinent to the explanation of human experience and behavior. If the first alternative is true, if man's responses are only special cases of physical interactions, then the relativity of time cannot apply to some physical systems, since to admit that it applies to man as a physical object would involve a denial of the obvious fact of the irreversibility of experienced time. But this is equivalent to saying that physical laws do not apply to all physical systems, and such contradictions we cannot consistently admit. If we assume the truth of the second alternative, we are confessing that materialism does not give us an explanation of human experience and conduct. But as soon as we admit that some (if not all) the laws of physics are irrelevant to psychological processes we open the road to the introduction of subjective experience into science. And if we adopt the evolutionary explanation of the origin of man the necessity for the introduction of animism and anthropomorphism into nature becomes still more apparent. If man's experiences and reaction patterns have their beginnings in more primitive organisms, where are we going to stop when we try to state where consciousness originates in the animal kingdom? Why stop at even the most primitive unicellular organisms? Perhaps the molecules of inorganic chemistry are organisms in some sense, and have a continuity of experience where past and future are marked off by a conscious present.

The reader may be inclined to object at this point: He would, for instance, like to have a definition of the term "physical" and "laws"; or perhaps he fails to see the force of our dilemma? No matter! All that we are trying to do is to open up the approach to a complete reconsideration of all our common sense and scientific notions. What we are now suggesting is that perhaps the modern clear cut distinctions between the physical and the psychical, the inanimate and the living, the unconscious and the conscious, are not so fundamental as we have hitherto considered them to be. More specifically, we are trying to pave the way for presenting the idea that even within the realm of physical reality we may have to introduce something analogous to mind and purpose.

There must be something in the universe, behind the observed processes and events of nature, analogous to that which we grasp as the irreversible flow of time. In such a view mind may be regarded as a form of time. If we are willing to reinterpret nature in accordance with some such plan as I have just suggested, the antithesis between the scientific and idealistic explanations no longer appears as an irreconcilable opposition.

Perhaps at this point it would be well to return to the foregoing dilemma and attempt to come to terms with it. We cheerfully concede that the doctrine of relativity, as a generalization in physics, is as applicable to the motions of a man's body (when his body is not taken as the center of reference) as it is to the motions of Mercury. But there are motions and motions, and each movement has a meaning of its own. Let us get some of these motions in mind, so to speak:

Motions in Space
{
Translatory
Rotary
Vibratory
Circulatory
Undulatory (simple harmonic, etc.)
}

When we are dealing with translatory or rectilinear motions (either with uniform velocity or with acceleration) there is no reason to deny the relativity of time and motion. Some experts have asserted that rotary motion is not relative, as Einstein asserts. I shall not attempt to pass judgment on that question. I do believe, however, that there is one type of motion which is absolute. *Growth* is a type of motion which is not relative. The test of growth and evolution is movement in the direction of increasing complexity of parts and harmony of functional organization. It is generally admitted that physical relativity has nothing to do with biological processes. I should even go further and argue that since we can consider that evolution and growth occur also in the inorganic world (*vide* "stellar evolution" and "atomic evolution"), relativity does not apply to all types of change and motion even within the domain of physics. If we assume that relativity refers to the motions which are described by the world-lines or geodesics of the four-dimensional space-time manifold, then growth is the expression of a fifth dimension to which present-day Einsteinian relativity does not apply. It is this unique dimension of growth which underlies the unidirectional or irreversible character of experience. But I shall have more to say of this later.

I wish to make it clear that in this view we are not asserting what many other well-intentioned harmonizers of religion and science seem to have in mind when they declare that there is no conflict when religion and science are "rightly understood." Persons who take this stand usually imply by this that there is no conflict because science and religion are not talking about the same things; they don't tread upon each other's toes because religion and science are working in different fields. This solution seems to me to consist merely in the repetition of an inane formula; it is a verbal smoke screen. Let us try not to degenerate into befogging the matter with such nebulosities. Of course religion and science are talking about the same world! What nonsense to say that the organism the behavior of which the psychologist is trying to explain is not the same organism which the theologian is studying and preaching to! Such an attitude is a confession of mental laziness: If the scientist and the theologian are working in different worlds it frees the servant of the Lord from the obligation of knowing what is going on in science, and the scientist from the obligation of taking an interest in religion—except when an anti-evolution legislature prevents him from teaching what he thinks to be the truth!

Instead of repeating vacuous platitudes let us try to fill in the outlines of a picture of nature which will satisfy the demands of the factual world of science, and still embody in our picture the ingredients and pigments which the poets and the idealists find in nature. That such a world exists is obvious from the fact that the organism which the physiologist studies is the same organism which expresses purposes in its responses. If physiological processes are physical processes (as I believe they are), then at least some physical processes are the carriers of that which in us appears as purpose. This appears to be a valid deductive argument. That the premises are also true is the thesis which I shall attempt to establish. Furthermore, we are not to be bulldozed by any Freudian psychoanalyst who would dismiss this reasoning (or that of anyone except himself) because it is a "rationalization" or "wishful thinking."

VII. The Renaissance of Animism

Why does physics give us such a poverty-stricken picture of physical reality? It is because the physicist believes that the invariability of the objective physical world, in contrast with the variability of the world of experience, proves that the content which is present in the consciousness is subjective, and therefore unreal physically. The assumption behind this is that the tests of physical or objective reality are the tests of the ease of measurement. Thus size and mass are regarded as primary qualities of matter because they are relatively easy to measure. We can also agree about the results. In case of failure to agree about the size or the mass of a body we can take a standard meter stick or scales and by actual measurement determine what the "real" facts are. The results are socially accessible to all. Since this is true the facts must be independent of our subjective point of view; the existence of these facts is not dependent upon our consciousness of these facts. Secondary qualities, on the other hand, are held to be subjective or in the minds of the observers because there is more variability in our conscious experiences of sensations. In case of dispute, as when a color blind person states that red and green strawberries look alike to him, whereas the "normal" person is convinced that they are of very different colors, it is difficult to compare experiences and settle the argument. Since the world of sensations is private to each individual, we conclude that these elements of consciousness do not inhere in the external world. Thus physics has excluded the study of qualities, and considers those things to be objectively real which can be measured.

This is a necessary and pragmatically useful abstraction which would work no harm if the scientist went no further. But he is then likely to continue, and assert that physics is the most fundamental science in existence because the data which is studied, *e.g.*, by psychology, is subjective and less real than the facts of physics. The viciousness of this idea becomes apparent when the behavioristic psychologist, wishing to appear scientific, then explains man in terms of physical notions, *and the physics he adopts is of the type which was deliberately fashioned by Newton and others to satisfy the dualism of mind and matter.*

In order to rebuild our theories of nature in such a way that we will not ignore the very real qualities which exist somewhere in nature we must retrace the history of modern physics and psychology. To achieve a view which will provide the stimulus for the release of æsthetic responses we must get the secondary qualities back into the external world. To those who are familiar with the ideas of A. N. Whitehead this is not an especially novel idea. A. S. Eddington also seems to be moving in the same direction when he tells us: "All through the physical world runs the unknown content which must surely be the stuff of our consciousness." Thus we see that the way has already been pointed out by some of the more daring of the physical philosophers.

That poetry has nothing to lose and everything to gain by an interpretation which repudiates the old materialism seems evident. Poets who are inclined to rhapsodize about the "light that never was on land or sea" have been inclined to criticize science because it would "untwist the rainbow." But this protest loses its force when we endow nature with those qualities which materialism explained out of existence. That it is possible for science to enrich our appreciations is the essence of the following lines:

> *Nor ever yet*
> *The melting rainbow's vernal tinctured hues*
> *To me have shown so pleasing, as when first*
> *The hand of science pointed out the path*
> *To which the sunbeams gleaming from the west*
> *Fall on watery cloud, whose darksome veil*
> *Involves the orient.*

In this hymn to the beauty of the rainbow it is clear
that a conception of physical reality is presupposed in
which qualities appear as ingredients of physical events.
This lends poetic support to our contention that it is possible to give an account of nature in terms of physics
and chemistry and still escape the barren dreariness of
an ancient and obsolete materialism. When we have
achieved the freedom from preconceived ideas which the
new interpretation of nature requires we will be able to
see poetry in the humblest of nature's garbs. Even so
common and nasty a stuff as coal-tar possessed inherent
beauty, as the following whimsical lines from *Punch* [2]
intimate:

> There's hardly a thing that a man can name
> Of use or beauty in life's small game
> But you can extract in alembic or jar
> From the "physical basis" of black coal-tar—
> Oil and ointment, and wax and wine,
> And the lovely colors called analine;
> You can make anything from salve to a star,
> If you only know how, from black coal-tar.

If further justification were needed to prove the possibility of interpreting the highest manifestations of nature in terms of physical chemistry we might secure that
justification in the fascinating ideas presented by Sir
Jagadis Bose, who perhaps is India's most distinguished
scientist. In the field of living matter this investigator is
advocating a view parallel to that which seems to be
argued for by Eddington and Whitehead in the domain
of what used to be called "lifeless" matter. Jagadis Bose
claims to have proved experimentally that plants can
feel; that, like animals, they have emotional responses.

[2] Quoted from William Foster's *The Romance of Chemistry*. 1927,
p. 378.

If the views of this scientist are correct we may conclude that plants fall in love, and that the death of one flower might cause another to pine away and die. As in the case of animals, their sentience could be abolished by the use of anæsthetics and drugs. This knowledge would be useful in transplantation, where anæsthetizing the plant with chloroform fumes would render it unconscious so that it would not feel pain when it is pulled up by the roots. These conclusions are based on the belief that plants have an elementary nervous system; that they breathe; and that they possess motile organs capable of responding to stimuli. In the words of Sir Jagadis Bose[3]: "The characteristics of conduction across the synapsoidal membrane in the plants are similar to those across the synaptic membrane in the animal."

This view, of course, runs counter to the notions implied or expressed in most modern text-books of botany.[4] For a biologist to declare that plants have souls would be to commit the unpardonable sin of anthropomorphism. And yet such a view does appeal to our poetic impulses. A florist, one suspects, would like to believe that flowers reciprocate his affection. And who is so unromantic that he would deny that this response from flowers to human beings, who lavish upon them their care, would add to the artistry of nature? Such a view recalls

[3] *The Nervous Mechanism of Plants,* 1926, p. 52.

[4] Among the astounding claims made by Bose is that in which he alleges that the sap which moves through the tree to the uppermost and outermost parts is pumped there by a heart-like action within the plant. But other investigators have failed to find this pulsating action, and some plant physiologists are asserting that these pulsations do not exist in the plants, but in the mind of Sir Jagadis himself. In view of the Oriental tendency towards pantheism which seems to envelop the speculations of this savant it would be well to withhold approval of his assertions concerning the nervous mechanisms of plants. This, however, does not constitute a retraction of any of the statements of the position of the present writer concerning the existence of directed response and purposive behavior in types of physical processes below animal forms.

the ideas of Fechner, who seriously put forth the view that plants have souls.

It is not at all clear that our own form of "anthropomorphism" commits us to the theory that plants have "souls," but it *is* clear that the time has come to take seriously the implications of evolution. In bringing physical nature and human nature closer together, evolutionary philosophy leaves us with the choice of mechanizing human nature or of vitalizing physical reality. I prefer the latter alternative.[5] We must rewrite our physics and our psychology, and in doing so we must tear down the walls which man has erected—especially where, as in the case of the distinction between the physical and the psychical, nature herself has placed no barriers.

[5] In this respect the present view has much in common with the panpsychism of Dr. Charles Hartshorne as embodied in his book on *The Philosophy and Psychology of Sensation* (1934).

CHAPTER II

MAN AND THE COSMOS

I. What Is Man?

IMMANUEL KANT, the Copernicus of modern philosophy, once exclaimed that two things moved him to wonder—the starry vault above and the moral law within. So fascinating to him was the canopy of the heavens that he was constrained to speculate about its origin; thus he was led to formulate the essentials of the theory which Laplace later presented in the form of the nebular hypothesis of the origin of the solar system. One might suppose that we, heirs to the age of Kant, would have even greater cause to marvel at the grandeur of the stellar universe, for astronomy since the age of Kant has greatly widened our purview of our cosmic environment. Curiously enough, however, the new knowledge of astronomy leaves us with mixed and confused views in some ways.

And this leads us to inquire: How fares it with that other source of wonder—the "moral law within"? Here, too, increasing knowledge of science has served—at least in the eyes of some—to dim the light of the moral sense, a jewel which Kant said shone by its own light! For modern biology and psychology have gone far since the days of Kant in explaining the sense of right and wrong, or the feeling of moral responsibility, in terms of the interactions of inherited modes of response, such as the instinct of "gregariousness," and the socially inherited customs of group life. As one writer has said, conscience is simply the echo of the tribal self.

We have referred to the interesting reversal of judgment since the days of Kant. It may be that this is so because man feels more and more his impotence in a universe of overpowering immensities. As the estimates of the age, size and mass of the universe increased, man appeared correspondingly to diminish in importance. This at any rate has furnished a factual basis for those authors who take delight in now portraying men as "lumps of impure carbons" crawling over the surface of one of the least and meanest of nature's many worlds. One of the classical pictures of man's insignificance in the universe of modern astronomy is given by Voltaire, who tells us in his romance, *Microméges*, of the visit of an inhabitant of the star, Sirius, to the earth. In the course of his excursion through interstellar space this giant, no less than five hundred thousand feet tall, makes the acquaintance of a man from Saturn. This individual complains because the people of Saturn have only seventy-two senses and live only fifteen thousand years, so that scarcely do the Saturnians begin to learn a little when death intervenes before they can profit by experience.

As these two extra-mundane travelers pass over the Mediterranean Sea the visitor from Sirius bends down and picks up a ship which he places on his thumb-nail for purposes of inspection—incidentally causing great excitement among the passengers of the vessel. The Sirian then felicitates the earth creatures on their supposed happiness in this world, but is told in reply by one of the philosophers that at that very moment "there are one hundred thousand animals of our own species, covered with hats, slaying an equal number of their fellow creatures, who wear turbans. . . ."

"Miscreants!" cried the indignant Sirian; "I have a good mind to take two or three steps, and trample the whole nest of such ridiculous assassins under my feet."

"Don't give yourself the trouble," replied the philosopher; "they are industrious enough in securing their own destruction."

Probably Voltaire is here indulging his sardonic wit, taking this means of expressing his contempt for man's stupidity, if not his cosmic insignificance.

But there is another way of looking at this matter. Rather than that man should be overwhelmed by the stupendous expanses of time and space, in which he appears as a trifling atom, should we not marvel at this ephemeral intruder in the cosmos who, by the power of thought, is able to grasp and understand in a measure this alien world about him?

Perhaps it is true that our respect for the "moral law within" has suffered an eclipse. But does this mean that man must forgo all pride in himself, lose all respect for human aspirations, and abandon the sense of momentous issues which has elevated him, at least in his own eyes, above the level of brute matter? When the light of the moral law within fails us, are we at a loss for sanctuaries? Surely we are not so impoverished! Why should we not erect in the place of the moral law the capacity to reason? Whatever its humble origins and present limitations, to the light of reason is due whatever progress the human race has achieved. It is that faculty which has enabled man to discover and in part explain the grandeur of the starry vault above. If the human mind can stand in awe only of incomprehensible figures, does man himself go begging for reverence? The story of the sciences that have made the study of the brain, the organ of the mind, their business may set us right in this.

First, however, let us survey the astronomical universe, the macrocosm, and then, by way of comparison, let us look inside the brain, that micro-universe which mirrors in miniature on the stage of consciousness the rôles enacted by the more heroic figures of the cosmic drama.

II. Atoms and Stars

In spite of the impressive increase of knowledge in the last several centuries concerning the outer universe in which we live, modern astronomy still leaves unanswered some most interesting questions. It is agreed that the stellar universe, no less than its counterpart, the infra-universe lying far beyond the powers of the ultra-microscope, consists mostly of empty space. As Emerson says:

> *Atom from atom yawns as far*
> *As man from earth, as star from star.*

If we could imagine a god totally outside our sidereal universe who was regarding the cosmos from an external viewpoint, it would appear as a fairly homogeneous crystal in which little bubbles, or what a cosmic geologist might call "faults" are observed. Such a being, were he far enough away, might also be able to determine the exact shape of this glassy sea of space. He would be able to settle a dispute which has appeared in recent years. Some astronomers hold that the cosmos is spherical in shape; others argue that it resembles a cylinder open at both ends towards plus and minus infinity. Still others—

fewer in number since Lemâitre has interpreted Einstein's theory of relativity to mean that the cosmos is a finite, but expanding, bubble—believe that the universe has no limits in any direction, and that the idea of *shape* is totally inapplicable to astral reality.

Whatever the truth in this matter may be, it is certain that here and there, scattered through the voids of space, there are aggregates of matter which project out of the emptiness like islands in a vast ocean. The figure is not inapt, for the larger flaws *are* island universes, and, all taken together, they make up the cosmos. These various island universes are made of many stars glued together, as it were, into vast, fiery ameba-like systems projecting their tenuous pseudopodia across trillions of miles of space. Each of these super-worlds is apparently like our own Milky Way, which is a galactic system, lense-like in shape, rotating about a center.

Let us now turn to a particular part of our own Milky Way, which is of unique interest to us. Here, about half way out from the center, which is supposed to be near the constellation Sagittarius, there is a smaller system called the solar system. This miniature universe consists of a star, our own *sun* in fact, around which revolve a number of planets in their respective orbits. One of these planets, the third removed from the sun and wheeling around in its elliptical path between Venus and Mars, is called the Earth. What is this pigmy among giants? Compared to other astral bodies the world is insignificant in size; and man, who lives his life on the surface of this tiny globe, appears as a kind of sub-atomic phenomenon amongst the whirling clouds of burning star-stuff. Out of star-dust he came; by star-light he lives; and into star-dust he must eventually dissolve—that is the verdict of modern science!

This thumb-nail sketch of man's place in the universe puts before us in pictorial form the facts as they are believed today. Astronomers deal with sizes and distances and times which are of such magnitude that the mind is dazed in trying to comprehend them. As we have seen, some have used these results as evidence of man's unimportance in the cosmic scheme of things. But since we now agree that the theological self-abasement which resulted from man's viewing himself as a "worm of the dust" and a "miserable sinner" was unwholesome—not to say hypocritical—may we not in a purely astronomical way have occasion for reconstructing our somewhat damaged superiority complex?

Let us reconsider the problem.

III. Quantity Versus Quality

In the first place, one may point out that mere size and massiveness are no test of significance. To counteract the force of the suggestion that "bigger" and "better" are synonymous, we need only remind ourselves of the view of the idealists that a single human being is worth an entire nebula of insensate electrons and protons. (Would that we always acted as if this were true!) But even admitting for the sake of argument that man's importance in the universe bears some relation to his size, how then does man stand? Perhaps our sense of perspective is restored if we look in the opposite direction, towards the infinitely little, instead of in the direction of galaxies and island universes. A drop of water contains so many atoms that their number is meaningless. And in comparison with a drop of water man is an exceedingly weighty issue, for he is composed of not less than four good buckets of water.

Such comparisons, while not æsthetically edifying, show us that whether we are to consider man as large or small depends entirely upon what he is being compared with. With respect to the micro-universe of molecules and atoms man is a veritable giant among dwarfs. If, therefore, man partakes somewhat of the nature of infinitesimals, he also partakes in no less degree of the nature of the infinitely great. In other words, man falls midway between two worlds, the infra-universe beyond the ultra-microscope, and the supra-universe studied by astronomy. Quantitatively this is quite accurate, for as Professor A. S. Eddington [1] has pointed out, about 10^{27} atoms make a man's body, while 10^{28} human bodies constitute enough material to build a star. Man lives his life in a middle-scale universe, suspended between two infinities, and he appears to possess qualities derived from both domains. The human brain, the most distinguishing feature of man, in a sense represents the cross-roads of the universe.

And now, in order to silence completely those who bow the head only in the presence of overpowering numbers, let us transport ourselves into that hidden kingdom which lies within the walls of our heads. In his book on *The Brains of Rats and Men*, Professor C. J. Herrick quotes one authority to the effect that there are twelve thousand million nerve cells, or neurones, in the brain. Professor Herrick then points out that the number of possible functional combinations or patterns of neuronic connections far surpasses any figure which astronomers have occasion to use in measuring astronomical distances. During a few minutes of the intense cortical activity involved in an act of thought the number of neural con-

[1] *Stars and Atoms*, 1927, p. 9.

nections employed may well exceed the total number of atoms in our solar system.

We see, therefore, that modern science, which has done so much to undermine the mediæval faith in the central importance of man in the drama of creation, is itself a silent eulogy on the creative power of thought in explaining the physical universe which still elicits our admiration. Kant, were he living today, instead of debating the problem, "How is metaphysics possible?" might well attempt to answer the question, "How is thinking possible?" A timid soul, contemplating the intricacies of the neural basis of thought, would shudder at the knowledge of the apparently infinite number of difficulties which must be overcome in our brains before we can think about the starry vault above, which is so imposing to some. Accordingly, Kant might rephrase his exclamation as follows: Two things move me to wonder—the starry vault above and the thinking brain within!

IV. Relativity, Behaviorism and Consciousness

To himself man has always been a problem, if not a paradox. To him his status in nature is the cosmic question mark. Is he an evanescent by-product of an indifferent nature, an excrescence from a meaningless whirl of mass-particles, who thinks he is free, and master of his destiny, only because of an egotism distilled by a physiological sublimation from biological instincts of survival and reproduction? Or does man possess within himself an immortal part, not subject to the ordinary laws of mechanics, which differentiates him from the brutes and gives him his mastery over nature? Or is man's power to reason, to hope, to anticipate the future, not a miraculous gift, but only an illustration of the universal physi-

cal laws operating in the very complex system of mechanical contrivances in the human nervous system? Is
the biologist correct when he says that life is a web on
the loom of time, and that so far as science can see, the
loom works automatically, the threads spin themselves?
But if this is true, how then does it happen that man
alone appears to be able to alter the spinning and the
pattern, so that as he spins he designs the web of the
future? How can an automaton discover the laws of its
own nature, and analyze the universe and master that
very nature of which it is an inextricable part?

The questions we have just posed remind one of the
seven world enigmas which Émil du Bois Reymond enun-
ciated at the end of the nineteenth century, of which he
prophesied that several would remain forever unsolved.
Among the insolubilia which he enumerated were the
problem of the nature and connection of matter and
force, and the problem of the origin of sensation and consciousness. Since the year this declaration was made
about half a century has elapsed. In the intervening
period almost all that forms the foundation of what is
sometimes termed the "new" physics has been discovered. It would be interesting to see whether this new
knowledge throws any light on those problems which
du Bois Reymond declared to be insoluble. First of all
let us glance at the situation in physics.

It is generally assumed that all that has appeared during the last five decades is an indication of the progress
that physics has made. And, in one sense, physics *has*
made astonishing advances. Certainly the discovery that
the atom is divisible—the formulation of the whole electron theory of matter—brings the scientist just that much
nearer the real facts about the ultimate structure of matter. But, the philosopher asks, are the physicists any

closer to the final truth, an adequate explanation of the entire domain of physical phenomena? This is a question which cautious physicists would not answer offhand. There is more modesty in claims among physicists today than there has been at any time in the past. If a realization of the limitations of human knowledge is a sign of progress, then surely physics has made progress!

There is another sense in which physics has made progress. If it is admitted that certain kinds of questions are insoluble because of the way in which they are stated, or if it is discovered that certain problems are *created* by the way in which we define our terms, and that therefore these problems vanish when we redefine our terms and restate our problems, then to abolish a problem by showing that it is really non-existent may also be taken as a sign of progress. And this, it seems, is exactly what has happened in physics. The first of the insolubilia of du Bois Reymond we have considered, that of the interaction of "force" and "matter," is solved in Einstein's theory of relativity when the concept of force is virtually abolished. The way in which this ancient problem is avoided is now generally understood.

And now let us pause to examine how psychology has fared within these same decades. Are the psychologists any closer to the solution of that other enigma, the problem of the origin of consciousness?

The problem of establishing the missing connections between the phenomena of consciousness and the rest of our scientific knowledge is beyond doubt the most important unsolved problem which faces contemporary theoretical science. It is not a paradox that this should also be the most difficult of the problems awaiting solution. Supposing—in an optimistic mood—that the solution will appear, will it come as a stroke of genius from one man, or as a gradual development of existing knowledge along established lines? Or will the progress to be made here in the solution of the psychophysical problem come as a result of a procedure similar to that which physics followed in abolishing the problem of the interaction of force and matter? If so, who is to be the Einstein of psychology who will devitalize the last surviving spirit ("force" or "cause") of ancient animism? At this point I am sure the name of the leader of the behavioristic movement, Dr. John B. Watson, will come into the mind —or the larynx—of some of my readers. And, in truth, what Dr. Watson and his followers propose to do in psychology is not so very different from what Einstein has done in physics. Just as the physicist ignores the ether of space as a privileged *frame of reference,* because it acts *as if* it does not exist, in the sense that its presence cannot be detected by any physical measurements, so in psychology mind is rejected by the behaviorist as a privileged *coördinate system,* because mind has never been isolated and measured objectively by any known instruments. The behaviorists assert that psychology can be made scientific only by renouncing all subjective methods and contributions. Physics is exalted as the ideal pattern of all science. Since consciousness, if it exists at all, is private, it cannot be made the subject matter for a scientific psychology. Thus argues the behaviorist.

Unfortunately for the behaviorist, the solution to the problem of consciousness is not as simple as all that. It is a significant fact that the physicist is less certain of the objectivity of physics than the behaviorist. The subjective element cannot be eliminated. This view has been reiterated time and again by A. S. Eddington, who asserts that it is the mind which isolates what it considers to be the permanent things in nature. If this view is the correct one, we may then conclude that no behaviorist is likely to turn out to be the Einstein of psychology.

We may, however, agree with the behaviorist that the problem of consciousness is insoluble in terms of the traditional distinction between mind and body. Conventional psychology developed around what has since turned out to be an obsolete physical theory. Matter has historically been conceived to be the seat or core of "primary" qualities; hence, almost by definition, body could not be identified with conscious experience, such as "redness," which was held to be a "secondary" quality in the mind. Thus the dualism of mind and matter has been *created by definition,* and is not a result of generalization from *observations of fact.* But the new physics now provides us with a theory of matter in which the gap between consciousness and matter may be more easily bridged. To discover how this synthesis may be attained is our problem to investigate in the following pages.

In carrying forward a program such as we have outlined, it is necessary to formulate answers to two main types of problems. The elaboration of a theory of man's place in nature involves the use of reason, and a "true" theory presupposes some notion of what we mean by truth. Furthermore, the theory one presents as true attempts to state what are the "real" facts about nature, what its causes are, etc. Thus every *cosmology,* or theory of man's place in the universe, embodies a theory of knowledge and truth (*epistemology*) and a theory of reality (*ontology*). That is:

Cosmology   { *Epistemology: theory of knowledge*
(theory of man
  and the universe) { *Ontology: theory of reality*

Of course one's theory of knowledge and theory of reality are intimately related, a fact which is illustrated by traditional systems of philosophy and taken for granted in the present exposition. Some scientists appear to believe that epistemological considerations are irrelevant in science, but that this is not the case is one of the things which, I trust, will appear in the following chapter.

CHAPTER III

THE CRISIS IN SCIENCE

I. Science and Civilization

The question is sometimes discussed as to which of the various inventions and discoveries of the human race has produced the greatest change in social life and action. If we are thinking of consequences largely practical in nature—those which modify our modes of life more than our habits of thinking—then this honor probably belongs to the invention of fire. But if we are thinking of the influence of rational doctrines, and confine ourselves to the culture of our own Western World, the choice probably lies between the following:

(a) the new cosmology of Copernicus, which replaced the older geocentric theory of astronomy established by Aristotle and Ptolemy;

(b) the Darwinian theory of evolution, which supplanted the "special creation" theory of the origin of species;

(c) the contemporary discoveries in physical science, which have resulted in Einstein's theory of relativity, the quantum theory of energy, and its offspring, wave mechanics.

Here, in the order of historical development, we undoubtedly have the three greatest discoveries of the human mind in the field of the sciences.

Without trying to decide the merits of the claims of

each of these aspirants to the position of first place in the domain of intellectual advance, let us here limit ourselves to a discussion of the influence of the idea of evolution on human thought. One reason for the power and the dominance of this idea lies in the fact that the implications and applications of the idea of evolution were not restricted to the field in which the idea first developed, in biology, but soon spread, so that the implications were almost immediately traced out and put to work in the fields of the various social sciences: history, anthropology, ethnology, philology, cultural sociology, and even religion.

Herbert Spencer, who was one of the first to outline an evolutionary social theory, looked upon social evolution as a movement towards a condition in which completely evolved organisms were adapted to a completely evolved society. In such a society, or utopia, all problems would vanish, since a problem by its very nature presents the need for a further adaptation. But if this is the ideal society, it is now quite certain that Spencer's ideal is impossible of attainment—at least if present tendencies are any indication of future probable conditions! For it now seems that as society evolves it creates new and more complex problems, which fill to overflowing the places vacated by the old problems which disappear in the onward march of the human race. It is entirely possible that society is getting so complicated, and the attendant problems becoming so numerous and perplexing, that society may eventually disintegrate from lack of unity and coördination of functions.

Today the world is confronted by problems such as no age or race of men has ever faced before. If society is to solve its problems and survive, we will of necessity be forced to discover principles of intellectual and social cohesion. We must find principles of synthesis which will give to society a sense of cultural continuity and assist human beings in creating a new world, a world in which natural science, social forces, and political organization will be better coördinated. But this brings us at once to the supreme difficulty which faces those who are attempting to lay the foundations for the new cultural synthesis. Every man is an inhabitant of three worlds: there is (1) the inner and private world of consciousness, with its inner fears, hopes, and aspirations; then (2) there is the physical world of the external environment, terrestrial and cosmic, studied by the natural sciences; and (3) there is the social world of other human beings, in which man must live and move. Man's problem is to live effectively in each of these three worlds, but as statistics of the inmates of insane asylums demonstrates, this is no easy task.

If the total universe in which man finds himself is to be a meaningful universe, and the life of each man to be significant, it is necessary that we reconstruct our interpretations of these separate universes in such a way that a harmonious interaction is possible. If this is ever to be attained the social sciences, the natural sciences, and psychology, that intermediate science which bridges the gap between the two, will be compelled to discover and formulate relevant principles of inter-relation. As yet, however, the social sciences have not been able to discover a dominant philosophy of society. The same is true of psychological science. And to complete the cultural synthesis there is also required an intellectually unified picture of our physical cosmos, with a correct conception of man's place in that universe. But thus far the natural sciences have not been able to frame any unitary scheme which can be integrated into our other knowledge. Such is the situation at the present time.

While we cry for interpreters, for scientific seers, who can lead us through the mazes of modern learning, our scientists remain philosophically inarticulate. The reason for this is in part as follows. There is no integration of knowledge, no unity of insight, because scientists themselves are overwhelmed by the intellectual Frankenstein monsters which they have called into being. The most striking feature about the development of the sciences in the last several centuries is just this ever-increasing acceleration in the accumulation of bewildering masses of detailed facts. Inevitably there has accompanied this increase in factual materials a corresponding increase in difficulty in synthesizing these facts into meaningful systems of knowledge. In enlarging the sphere of knowledge by the discovery of new facts science has certainly made progress. But it is doubtful whether science has made progress towards a better understanding and explanation of the various domains of natural phenomena. To be sure, there is the synthesis which occasionally appears in the form of a synoptic vision of a Darwin or an Einstein, but the physical, social, and biological sciences still lack unifying principles of inter-relation. In a general way it sometimes appears as if every extension by science of the *outer boundary of the sphere of the known* is but an enlargement of the *inner boundary of the sphere of the unknown.*

In order that our summary of the situation may not appear to be unfair, or based on vague generalities, let us present the case in the form of several specific instances of our thesis, as follows:

(1) Science, following the maxim of "divide and conquer," has created fields so highly specialized that two persons working in different fields, or investigators working in different branches of the same field, are no longer able to understand each other. Perhaps we need a new logical technique of communication, as some thinkers believe; but the very least that we require is a corresponding integration of results to keep pace with the specialization of interest and results.

(2) Science has increased its practical control over physical nature, and extended its ability to predict and anticipate the future, but we have no adequate and generally accepted theory of natural law which explains and justifies those results. The status of induction, causality, probability, etc., is a scandal in the philosophy of science.

(3) In its practical applications science is giving us more and more of material and economic goods, and is influencing our external modes of living at an ever-accelerating rate, but at the present time it gives us little intellectual insight, or unity of outlook on nature. Moreover its technique for the social control of its own products has lagged woefully behind. Science needs to be humanized and socialized before it becomes an unadulterated benefit to mankind.

(4) The development of science has brought us to certain paradoxes which threaten to discredit science as a theoretical pursuit. Thus, for example, mathematics is still as useful as ever, but its very foundations are being shaken by the spread of skepticism. For example, the status of the fundamental concept of infinity, and the paradoxes of the theory of aggregates, are endangering the superstructure of mathematics and science.

We shall return to some of these problems at a later stage. Now let us, in the remainder of this chapter, examine one proposed solution to a certain class of problems which is foremost in science at the present time.

II. PHYSICS AND THE LAWS OF THOUGHT

The singular situation which is arising in modern physical science is doing more than affecting the fundamentals of physics. Scientists are deeply perturbed because they are forced, at different times, to use theories which are mutually incompatible. Consider the parlous state of affairs: Is there an ether of space? If so, is the ether stationary, or does moving matter drag the ether along with it? When a bar of metal is moving with enormous velocity in the direction of its length, does it actually suffer the contraction posited by Fitzgerald? Or is this an Einsteinian effect, produced by the relativity of space and time? Is this contraction, whether real or fictitious, precisely of the amount necessary to account for the negative result of the famous Michelson-Morley experiment? Is it true that nature does in fact conspire against the scientist to defeat his utmost efforts to determine an absolute velocity through space, or the ether? And, if necessitated by experiment, could Einstein's theory be reconciled with the possibility that the velocity of light is not constant, but varying? Would the proof that the velocity of light is not constant make it necessary to return to some form of ether theory? How can an electron be a tiny point-charge, and yet have an electromagnetic "field" extending to infinity, if there is no ether, and if space is not infinite, but finite—whether expanding or not? And how can an electron be at once corpuscular and an undulation?

These are some of the questions agitating science. Are the physical theories wrong? Or must we overhaul the foundations of logic to find the source of our difficulties, as Count Alfred Korzybski [1] holds? Modern science, torn

[1] In his book, *Science and Sanity: An Introduction to Non-Aristotelian Systems and General Semantics,* 1933, the Science Press.

between allegiance to traditional modes of thought and loyalty to "nasty little facts," is coming to suspect that we will either have to revise these modes of thought or ignore facts which appear to violate conventional notions of what is rational and possible. The facts to which we refer, which have brought science to its present heretical tendencies, are in the main those which underlie the development of micro-physics. Particularly disturbing to conventional modes of thought and explanation are the more recent discoveries indicating that the old dichotomy of physical phenomena into waves (or undulations) and particles (or corpuscles) is no longer satisfactory. Facts show that particles may simulate the properties of waves (radiation) and waves may exhibit the properties of particles. The breakdown of this division is disconcerting, for an antinomy at the very foundation of physical reality may disturb the entire superstructure.[2]

It was to be expected that among the suggestions concerning the fundamental difficulty of reconciling the conventional concepts of thinking with the realities of microphysics would be the proposal that the trouble lies within the thinking apparatus we employ in trying to understand these new physical phenomena. The suggestion is now definitely in the air that the difficulties in physics in the last few years are due to the fact that physicists are trying to deal with an entirely new set of physical phenomena in terms of an old logic, devised to fit a world quite different from the infra-universe of atomic physics.

At present the best doctrine for dealing with these new phenomena is found in wave mechanics, but this appears to involve a departure from the old logic. Ac-

---

[2] Dirac's theory of radiation probably comes closest to removing successfully the contradiction between waves and particles, and yet this is certainly not the last word that will be said on this subject.

cording to the old logic, if an entity is a particle, it is a particle; and if it is a wave phenomenon, it is a wave phenomenon. This is an application of the *law of identity, A is A*. The *law of excluded middle* states that *A*, any physical entity, is either a particle or not a particle (*i.e.*, it cannot be both); and the *law of contradiction* says that a particle cannot be non-corpuscular. These laws were held to be not only laws of thought, but also laws of physical reality and fully "obeyed" by nature. According to traditional logic a thing cannot both be a certain phenomenon (a particle) and not be it (*i.e.*, be something else, like a wave). But when Schrödinger treats an electron as if it were an undulation, he seems to be saying that a physical phenomenon can be both corpuscular and non-corpuscular, and this seems to be equivalent to saying that *A is both B and non-B*.

This is a specific illustration. But in general modern physics seems to be paying less attention to traditional fashions in thinking. Not only are old concepts and definitions being revised, but the old axioms of physics are falling into disrepute. But first let us set down what appear to be these axioms of traditional physics. They have to do with the most elementary relations between things in space and time. Here are some of them:

1. *Whatever is, is.*
2. *A thing is what it is.*
3. *A thing is where it is.*
4. *The same thing cannot be in two different places at the same time.*
5. *Two different things cannot be in the same place at the same time.*
6. *In order that a thing can get from one place to another, it must move through the intervening space, and it must take a finite amount of time to do this.*

In the new theories every one of these axioms is either denied or thrown open to question. In the first place, it may be argued, the statement that a thing is what it is is useless, if not untrue. Take the electron, for example. We now know that the electron is not a sharply delimited, self-sufficient-thing-in-itself, separated from other such entities by empty space. It is a nodal point in the field of energy, a dynamic center of relations which pervade the spatio-temporal field in which it acts. It is not even correct to say that the electron *has* a field, for it *is* the singularity within the field. On this matter the idea stated by Weyl [3] does not need to be revised. As he says, "Just as the theory of relativity has taught us to reject the belief that we can recognize one and the same point in space at different times, *so we see that there is no longer any meaning in speaking of the same position of matter at different times.*"

A second reason for doubting the law of identity as a law of nature (but not as a law of thought) arises in connection with the fact that, as Whitehead [4] points out, "every actual entity is in its essence social and requires the society in order to exist. In fact, the society for each entity is the all-inclusive universe." This means that the properties a thing exhibits depend not only on the intrinsic nature of the thing itself, but also on the environment it is in. The best that we can say is that the "thing" is the more or less permanent possibility of behaving in certain ways in different environmental settings.

The third reason for questioning the law of identity, that a thing is what it is, is that in an evolving world things change, and as soon as you specify by definition

[3] *Space-Time-Matter*, by Hermann Weyl, Eng. Trans., 1922, p. 202.
[4] *Religion in the Making*, by A. N. Whitehead, p. 106. See also *Process and Reality, passim.*

the properties of an electron, the thing, as a result of trafficking with a new environment, may take on or exhibit properties not stated in the definition. There is no evidence that electrons are ever exactly alike; history may play a rôle in determining even the properties of individual electrons: thus Whitehead argues that an electron within the human body behaves differently from an electron outside the body. The statement that a thing is what it is reminds one of the old Greek paradox attempting to prove that motion is impossible by arguing that a thing must either move where it is, or where it isn't, but since it can't move where it is, and can't move where it is not, motion is therefore impossible! This leaves out the third possibility, that motion is precisely the process whereby a thing gets from where it was to where it is (or wasn't). In the same way, the statement that a thing is what it is may leave out the possibility of the thing which, over a period of time, passes from what it was to what it wasn't. From the point of view of the law of identity the electron cannot evolve, and it either exists or does not exist. The possible intermediate case of the creation of an electron (not necessarily out of "nothing," but out of the electromagnetic field of energy), this involving a temporal process, is not provided for. And yet there may be a condition in which it is legitimate to say that the electron partly exists and partly does not exist. You cannot specify the properties of a thing in terms of an instantaneous snapshot of it. A thing is what it is, to be sure, but what is it?—if it is!

The remainder of these "axioms" require little comment. Since, in the theory of wave mechanics, the field of an electron extends to infinity, this means that the electron is larger than the atom of which it is a constituent and thus the fields of electrons interpenetrate. An electron, therefore, exists in every place where its effects extend—though the electrical density is concentrated in greatest amount at those nodal points called "particles" —and in this sense the same thing may be in two different places at the same time. By the same logic it follows that two different things may be in the same place at the same time.

Thus it appears that traditional logic is violated in micro-physical reality. This conclusion, however, does not mean necessarily that it is imperative that in our revision of logic we discard the *laws of thought*. These laws express the state of affairs in an ideal and timeless world, where things do not change and evolve. From the point of view of pure logic the natural world may appear to contain an irrational element, but to transfer this imperfection to the domain of logic itself is to allow logic, in the service of science, to become our master rather than our servant. That something can be done to perfect our tools is granted, and one direction in which this improvement may be made lies in the development of a statistical theory of classes. In the next section we shall sketch the main outlines of a possible development along such lines.

III. A Statistical Theory of Classes

It is one of the curious facts of human nature that some of the most powerful tools of the human intellect are also the source of much difficulty. Thus the human thinker can do something which unthinking matter cannot: he can *fixate* the essence of a thing by definition. This is the intellectual analogue of what the biologist does when he fixes a preparation by staining. This is perhaps the source of our difficulty in reconciling the world of thought with the world of things. Plato long ago made the distinction between the timeless world of mathematical universals, eternal and changeless, and the changing world of sensible particulars. In the Platonic realm of *archetypes* time does not enter; for a Platonist it is nonsense to talk about the "evolution" of mathematical truths, since the Ideas, like the number-patterns of Pythagoras, are static. But while these entities of pure logic and mathematics have *form*, they have no empirical *content*, and the natural scientist, finding empirical content in this world of changing physical realities, insists upon giving content to the form and form to the content. Alas, however, he then finds that his application of the terms (classes) defined by the fixative method gets him tangled up in the problem of reconciling change with permanence, content with form, time with eternity. Thus epistemological problems force themselves upon the scientist so that, almost against his will, he is forced to philosophize.

The facts of motion, change, and growth have always presented difficulties to the human mind. If the world were completely static and changeless, like Plato's realm of archetypes, there would be no problem of reconciling the logic of thought with the logic of reality. But since nature does undoubtedly evolve, we face the difficulty which Zeno and Hegel recognized, but attempted to solve in different ways. Zeno's paradoxes of motion, designed to prove that motion is impossible and that our senses are only deceiving us when they report motion and change, present an alternative to the Hegelian approach. Hegel disposed of the problem of change and evolution by cheerfully admitting the contradictory element in processes of development and by abandoning the law of excluded middle, except as a law of *abstract* reason. Bertrand Russell, advocating another solution, holds that Zeno's "paradoxes" are solved by the mathematical theory of *infinity* and *continuity*. Curiously enough, the notion of the infinite in turn leads to certain mathematical antinomies. Here we may refer to the proposal of L. E. J. Brouwer [5] to avoid the difficulties of the mathematical infinite by rejecting the law of excluded middle. Thus on either Hegel's evolutionary theory or Brouwer's view the time-honored law of excluded middle is set aside.

Part of the problem of reconciling the world of concepts with the world of percepts, or of adjusting the domain of mathematics to the realm of empirical nature, lies in a revision of the fundamental notion of *class*. Let us begin by defining a class, after the fashion of symbolic logic, as the group of individuals satisfying a *propositional function*.[6] However, the members of the corresponding empirical collection are never exactly alike, but are instances of the class in most respects. Each member of the class is a unique individual, and in its properties fluctuates about the statistical average. Thus the concepts and terms symbolizing a class refer to the *central tendency* of a frequency distribution, and at the two ends of the curve the behaviors of the individuals depart markedly into a "twilight zone." In this zone we have the irrelevant features and fluctuations peculiar to the individuals along the borderline of the transitions into neighboring classes. Thus Pithecanthropus Erectus is on the borderline between the anthropoid apes and Homo Sapiens. From this point of view new species in biology represent statistical fluctuations in the unit characters

[5] For a statement of Brouwer's views see Max Black's volume, *The Nature of Mathematics*, or the writer's paper, "Non-Aristotelian Logics," *Monist*, 1935, Vol. xlv, 100-118.

[6] Propositional functions are discussed in R. M. Eaton's text, *General Logic*, and L. S. Stebbing's *A Modern Introduction to Logic*.

(genes) sufficiently great to mark the appearance of sizable novelties, and thus new classes appear as "cuts" in a statistical ensemble. New classes may therefore be regarded as beginning at the points where the tangents to the curve of distribution change direction. Since the number of variants becomes smaller as the mutations become larger (as more extreme fluctuations in the statistical distribution), the fertility of nature is necessary to secure the "population density" essential to the production of the relatively small number of mutants with differences in structure and function sufficiently large to constitute the beginnings of new species (classes).

And now we come to a more philosophical phase of our reconstruction. The fact of evolution, by virtue of which new species (classes) are produced, suggests that every "finite" growing thing partakes of the nature of the "infinite," in the sense that it possesses possibilities (potentialities) which, in Aristotelian language, can be realized. Every organic whole is something more than the linear sum of the properties of its parts, in that there is something in it which endows it with the property of an infinite aggregate of mathematics. Just as assertions about the properties of finite classes cannot be made to apply to transfinite aggregates, so in a similar way the peculiar non-additive properties of an emergent whole (gestalt) cannot be predicated of the constituent parts. This may seem like a far-fetched analogy, but no less an authority than A. N. Whitehead regards the domain of the infinite as the realm of possibility. In physical science the ether of space was the older physical repository of potentialities, the realm of infinity and continuity. But even though, in accordance with relativity theory, we dispense with that last "eminent victorian," it still remains true that the continuity characteristic of an infinite aggregate (a *dense* series, in the case of a mathematical line) appears in physical processes in the dynamic interaction whereby microscopic ensembles enter into the formation of new wholes. Thus it becomes possible to apply a mathematics of continuous quantities, the differential equations of hydrodynamics, to the behavior of water, since physically there is present something which is analogous to mathematical continuity, due probably to the interaction between overlapping fields of force.

In order to bring these conclusions to a focus on our original problem of relating the laws of logic to physical reality, let us now restate our position. Our contention is that if change is the realization of possibility, and if the realm of possibility is the domain of infinity, then anything that exists takes on the appearance of possessing contradictory properties as soon as the thing is defined in terms of any given set of properties. That is, an organic thing is what it is because of the environment it is in, and we can define it only by limiting its properties to those exhibited in some specified (finite) environment. But all organic things share in the nature of infinity, in the sense that in different environmental settings they "go beyond themselves" in expressing new properties, as compared with the properties manifested under other conditions. In Hegelian terms, each empirical thing is a union of interacting opposites, the opposites being the thing itself and the environment it is in. Out of the interaction a new synthesis may appear providing the basis for further departures. For this reason the law of excluded middle does not apply to empirical nature with absolute accuracy. There is always a margin of error, and our problem as methodologists is to form our classes and frame our definitions in such a way that they incorporate those properties which occur most frequently in the *average* situations (environments) within which the entities of the class of objects are normally found.

IV. EPISTEMOLOGICAL ASSUMPTIONS

We here summarize the foregoing epistemological theory as follows.

(1). Science presupposes abstraction. By a process of abstraction we isolate "things" from their environments and then define these entities in terms of what appear to be their essential properties. Both perception and conception stratify and "fixate" processes ("events" in the theory of relativity) into permanent and identical elements.

(2). Any abstracted element is *different from* the parts *into which it is analyzed,* not only because the properties of the whole may be *more than* the sum of the properties of the constituent parts, but also because the whole considered (abstracted) is a part of a more inclusive whole (eventually the entire cosmos). The whole is what it is because of its relation to inferior and superior levels, and these relations, being immaterial, are not readily seen.

(3). Even though the *number of elementary constituents* of the universe (electrons, protons, neutrons, etc.) be *finite,* the *number of possible relations* into which these constituents enter may be *infinite.*

(4). In the foregoing statement we do not necessarily assume that the "infinite" is an entity. The proposition still stands even though we substitute the "unlimited" for the "infinite." If we define the infinite in terms of the "operational" method of P. W. Bridgman, it becomes a name for a *non-terminating process.*

(5). Change is the process whereby *relata* enter into different *relations*. From the Aristotelian viewpoint, change may be defined as the passage from *potentiality* to *actuality*. If, as Professor Whitehead argues, the realm of possibility is the realm of infinity, a logic based on the *law of identity* is inadequate as a law of reality, though it still is valid as a law of abstract thought and still retains a pragmatic value in our adjustments to nature, at least so long as the limits of its empirical inaccuracy do not exceed certain bounds.

Having thus laid bare the epistemological presuppositions of our theory of knowledge, we are now prepared to undertake the formulation of a theory of reality.

CHAPTER IV

VISION AND REALITY

I. The Scientific Reformation

It is undoubtedly true that the present period represents the most profound reorganization of scientific theory the world has ever seen. It is not at all clear just what the positive outlines of the new philosophy of nature will be, but of one thing we are certain: another fossil of human intellectual evolution, the naïve materialism which modern physical science inherited from classical Greek atomism, will soon take its place in the cultural museum of deceased scientific doctrines.

If one inquires into the reasons for the decline of the doctrine of mechanistic materialism to which modern science has hitherto been wedded, the answer is readily discovered: it is to be found in the appearance of two revolutionary conceptions, namely, Einstein's theory of relativity and the quantum theory of energy. It is the well-weighed opinion of many scientists that of these two doctrines, the quantum theory of energy is likely to be the more revolutionary, even though, thus far, it has attracted less general interest than Einstein's more famous theory. According to Sir James Jeans,[1] one of the services of wave mechanics is that it calls attention to the inadequacy of the older space-time picture of physical reality. He tells us that our thoughts have become

[1] *The New Background of Science,* 1933, p. 252.

space-time bound, and that the abandonment of a space-time representation of nature is the first step on the road to a better understanding of nature. Space-time, Sir James states (p. 259), is not the framework of the world of nature, but the world of our sense perceptions. The events which affect our senses are only the outer surface of nature—like ripples on the surface of a stream—but the origins of these surface disturbances go deep down into the stream.

If we seek to understand how this conventional framework of science was developed in the first place, it will probably be found that the predominance of sensory perception in determining the course of reason has been especially important in stabilizing this doctrine as a dogma of science. As we have insisted before, we live our lives in a middle-scale universe, about half way between the infinitely little and the infinitely large. Our senses have evolved so that we may live effectively and propagate our kind in this average-sized universe. If we want to know what the nature of the things lying on either side of us may be, in the micro-universe beneath us or in the macro-universes above us, we must imaginatively construct our pictures from the forms and images which confront us in our middle-scale universe. We perceive this universe through the medium of that little band of visible light which strikes the eyes. The patterns of the physical objects in the external world are transmitted by light to the retina; this retinal mosaic is then converted into a code of nerve currents and conveyed up the optic nerve through subcortical tracts into the occipital cortex; and then by some subtle alchemy of nature the mind's eye sees and interprets the code and finds the proper response and conveys this to the motor areas. In extrapolating our images of nature into unexplored regions, the mind, by some kind of projective geometry, draws in imagination the outlines of atomic solar systems and cosmic systems. And there's the rub! If our senses do not positively deceive us, they at least are not always reliable guides in these strange and unsurveyed regions. In other words, our conceptual vision has been partially distorted by perceptual vision. Is it not possible, therefore, that it was this reliance upon the validity of visual experience which led to some of the problems which have perplexed modern physics?

As an illustration of what we have in mind consider the following case: Our eyes tell us that matter and empty space, in which the non-material waves of various types of frequencies are transmitted, have nothing in common; our brains have evolved around our eyes (or *vice versa*), and accordingly our thinking machinery has developed a logic of the physical world after the fashion of the engineer's blueprints. But now this world of intellectual constructions turns out to be inadequate when applied to other reaches of reality. However, the new modes of thinking which lie behind the theory of quanta and relativity doctrine indicate that men are not entirely the victims of their senses. We are slowly emancipating ourselves from the engineer's constructions. We are beginning to see the way to correct some of the imaginative pictures which have provided the scaffolding of science and to realize the truth of the doctrine of Jeans that while the older particle (material) picture presupposes the possibility of representation in space and time, the wave theory of matter implies the impossibility of understanding nature in terms of the sensory pictures of the ordinary space and time of perceptual experience.

The revision of our conception of physical nature which is made necessary by the recent developments in science must of necessity have repercussions in coming modifications of psychological and philosophical doctrines. It is one of our purposes here to try to formulate some general ideas about the broader implications of the scientific reformation. We are especially concerned with the bearing of these matters on what philosophers call the "problem of reality," a problem which has perplexed human beings ever since the dawn of rationality.

II. The Problem of Reality

In order to get launched into our subject, let us ask: What, then, *is* this problem of reality? Replying briefly, and in the language of philosophy, we may give the usual answer that *the problem of reality is concerned with trying to discover what we mean when we say that a thing is real*. Ordinarily a thing is said to be "real" when it is believed to *exist*. But then the next question is: *When does a thing exist?* What is the criterion we employ in distinguishing between the real and the unreal, the existent and the non-existent? For the present let us leave this question unanswered, in order that we may first consider the conditions under which this problem is likely to arise in a clearly articulated form.

In the history of Occidental philosophy the problem of reality did not make its appearance until the time of the early Greek philosophers, about the year five hundred B.C. It seems to be agreed that primitive man was not much given to philosophical speculation, so that for him there was no problem of reality. It is also assumed by many philosophers that unsophisticated persons living today (the "men of the street") resemble more primitive men in their outlook on the world. The attitude of both is supposed to be similar in that neither of them is aware of the existence of any "problem of reality." The technical term which is used to designate this prephilosophical attitude toward the world is *naïve realism*. The attitude of naïve realism may be summed up in the following two propositions:

1. *Things are what they are perceived to be. The rose is red, and the "redness" is as much a part of the rose as its size or shape. A thing has in fact the qualities it appears to have.*
2. *Perceiving or knowing an object makes no difference to the object that is perceived or sensed in any way.*

These are the two propositions on which the attitude of the unreflective individual is supposed to be based. Here there is no distinction between *appearance* and *reality* and a thing is asserted to be in fact what it appears to be.

In order to show that thinking about philosophical problems is not a waste of time, the philosopher next takes pleasure in demonstrating just why this attitude of naïve realism cannot be maintained on a rational level. He proceeds to show how and why naïve realism breaks down.

One way of showing the necessity for making a distinction between what a thing *appears to be* and what it *really is* consists in pointing to the various types of illusions and hallucinations to which men are subject. The psychologists have now classified many types of misperceptions (visual illusions, etc.), and in each case the principle that a thing is what it appears to be is violated. In general the procedure consists in showing that the idea of the naïve realist, that in the act of knowing the perceiver contributes nothing to the external phenomenon, is false. The philosopher who denies the validity of the principles of naïve realism tries to show that the world we live in arises out of two factors, the *environment* and the *organism.* Our perceptions of, and beliefs about, reality are a function not only of the external world as such, but also of the human individual. In other words, what we call reality cannot be completely described in terms of external objects alone. Here is an analogy for the two-term relation we have in mind: the tides of the earth cannot be explained in terms of the earth alone, nor in terms of the influence of the moon alone. The tides are a function of the inter-relation of the earth and the moon, and neither must be neglected or reduced to terms of the other.

In order to explain and amplify the statement that the perceived world arises out of the relational dependence between individuals and their external environments the following types of relative interdependence will be elaborated. The main types of relativity are: (1) *physical relativity,* (2) *biological relativity,* and (3) *psychological relativity*. It is possible, of course, that the third type of relativity is but a special case of the second type, and that this, in turn, is reducible to the first type; but for the present we will consider each of them as *sui generis.* Let us consider the bearing of physical relativity upon the problem of reality.

III. Physical Relativity

As an instance of the qualities of objects as dependent upon physical relativity consider the phenomenon of color. Astronomers classify stars into different groups, and a color classification would give us red, yellow, and blue stars. The naïve realist would say that a star which *appears* red *is* red. But the astronomer knows that the color of a star depends in part upon the relative movement of a star with respect to an observer on the earth. Here what the physicist calls the *Doppler effect* manifests itself. If a star is moving away from the earth fewer light waves will reach the observer in a unit interval of time than if the star were moving towards the earth. In this case there would be a shift in the spectrum towards the violet end. For the same reason, if an auto driver on the surface of the earth could approach a traffic light which is showing red with a sufficiently high velocity, the red light would appear green to him. If he could accelerate his velocity still further, all the lights (red, yellow and green) would be shifted into the ultraviolet (or invisible) region of the spectrum, and such inconveniences as traffic lights would cease to exist for the autoist. Of course, such high velocities are impossible on the surface of the earth, but exactly the same phenomenon occurs with sound (the velocity of which is much less than that of light), and every motorist has noticed the change in pitch of sound as another car sounding its horn, or train blowing its whistle, sweeps past him. Astronomers, however, do have to deal with the influence of relative velocity in determining whether a star is "really" red or not. We see, therefore, that the color of an object is not an absolute property of the thing perceived. This is called physical relativity because, as thus stated, it does not rest upon anything peculiar to the living organism. A photographic plate sensitive to color would react in the same way as an organism.

Modern physics now recognizes that in making a report about physical reality the rôle of the observer cannot be completely ignored. Physicists admit that one of the consequences of the theory of relativity has been to throw in doubt the assumption that such physical quantities as length, mass, potential, etc., are absolute and objectively invariant existents. Physical magnitudes are not properties of external objects alone, but are relations between these objects and the particular frames of reference from which they may be viewed and measured. Even the *shape* of an object is to some extent relative, for a spherical body appears to be flattened when viewed from a system moving at right angles to that body.

This fact that the rôle of the observer is not to be neglected is brought out in a new and interesting way in the new quantum theory. We are now told that measuring, or even perceiving, a phenomenon alters it, for observation always involves an interaction of light between the observer and the observed. In other words, a thing that has been observed is different from what it would have been if it had not been observed. We must not forget, however, that while physics may not be able to eliminate completely the observer, it can standardize his rôle. Indeed, the theory of relativity is one device for stating the laws of nature in such a fashion that they are independent of any particular frame of reference.

Let us now turn to considerations of biological relativity.

IV. BIOLOGICAL RELATIVITY

The first type of relativity is based upon the relation of the perceiver's frame of reference to that of the object viewed. The second type of relativity is based upon the biological constitution of the organism that does the perceiving. It is common knowledge that we perceive the external world through our senses. As Sir Jagadis Bose has said: "Out of the imperfections of his senses man has built himself a raft of thought to venture into the seas of the unknown." The idea that the way in

which the world appears is a function of the sensori-
motor organization of the organism is not new; nevertheless the general importance of this has not been sufficiently realized. In our discussion of this subject we shall
in the main be concerned with the importance of vision,
since it is this sense organ which contributes most to our
perceptual information about the world, and conse-
quently to our formulation of theories about the world.[2]
   We live in a world of physical objects, a world of trees,
hills, clouds, bodies of water, and so on. Many of these
objects appear to be fairly stable and solid. Let us consider one such familiar physical object—say this table
before us. We perceive the table before us in three dimensional space. Here at the very outset we face a difficulty.
The common sense idea that there is no problem about
the perception of an object in three dimensional space is
challenged by Professor Swann,[3] who points out that the
impression we get of an object which we see on the other
side of the room is derived from *two*-dimensional images
of it on the retinas of the two eyes. As Professor Swann
says, "I am worried, because I know that I see the stool
[table] upside down, that I see it twice over, and that
what the right eye sees the left-hand side of the brain
interprets. My contemplation of the stool is really a ter-
ribly complicated business." This presents initial grounds
for wondering how we ever get order out of such a situation, but does not warrant the belief that in this perceptual interpretation of the external world the organism
adds anything extra. This next step can be taken by
quoting from Bertrand Russell's [4] analysis, as follows: "To
the eye or to the touch, ordinary matter appears to be

   [2] On this matter note what Bertrand Russell has to say in his book,
The Analysis of Matter, Ch. XIV.
   [3] *The Architecture of the Universe*, by W. F. G. Swann, 1934, p. 253.
   [4] From the *A B C of Atoms*, p. 1.

continuous; our dinner-table, or the chairs on which we sit, seem to present an unbroken surface. We think that if there were too many holes the chairs would not be safe to sit on. However, science compels us to accept a quite different conception of what we are pleased to call 'solid' matter; it is, in fact, something like the Irishman's definition of a net, 'a number of holes tied together with pieces of string.' Only it would be necessary to imagine the strings cut away until only the knots are left." It seems, therefore, that there are really two tables, as Eddington [5] also recognizes. Let us set down the contrasts between the two, as follows:

The Table—

(A) As the ordinary perceptual object:
1. Appears to be hard and impenetrable
2. Is apparently inert and passive
3. Has a color, shape, texture, etc.

(B) As a scientific object:
1. Is composed mostly of empty space
2. In its microscopic constituents is as energetically active as it appears to be passive and inert
3. Perhaps does not have the color it appears to have. That is, the sensory qualities may not be *in* the table, and there may be properties in the table which our senses do not report to us. Thus there are atomic and molecular fields of force (electrostatic and electromagnetic) which bind the electrons and protons together into atoms and atoms into molecules.

Indeed, the more one thinks about the two tables the further apart the ordinary table and the scientific table become. Perhaps it has never appeared as mysterious that the ordinary solid and rigid table should emerge

[5] *The Nature of the Physical World,* by A. S. Eddington, 1928, p. ix.

from the mad dance of the atoms and molecules into which the table is resolved upon chemical and physical analysis. But consider: what is this property of *rigidity?* Sir Oliver Lodge has said that it is still a problem why, if we pick up one end of a ruler, the other end follows! We say that the ruler is "rigid," but we know that no two atoms or molecules are in actual contact. What, then, binds them together? Someone once remarked that it doesn't make much difference which end of a street car we get off of, because both ends usually stop at the same time; but why this is the case no one has ever completely explained. Here, as in so many other cases, familiarity breeds contempt. We do know, however, that progress in science shows us that under the X-ray eyes of science the solid table disappears, and this leads us to the conclusion that the perceptible properties of this "too, too solid" universe arise out of the limitations of our sense organs.

V. Vision and Thought

After contemplating for a moment this fact that what we call solid matter is composed mostly of "empty" space, one is led to ask how it happens that visual perception gives us one impression of the external world, while physical science, which in its imaginative constructions goes behind the gross world of the engineer, yields another and quite different account. In a general way it is undoubtedly true that the necessity for survival has contributed to the development of a set of sense organs which fit animals to get along as physical objects in an environing world of other physical objects. But the specific details of the story of this evolution still remain to be stated.

The human being, like other organisms, perceives best that world of objects in which he must live and move; or, conversely, given certain biological mutations, he will survive in that world for which he is best equipped, by virtue of his sensori-motor equipment, to adjust himself. If, as previously insisted, man's senses have been evolved so that he is fitted to function effectively in the middle-scale universe of the engineer—midway between the infra-universe of atoms and the supra-universe of stars—he must of necessity be able to perceive the familiar bodies of our environment in such a way that he can act upon them as things. The brain, the eyes, and the musculature are mutually interacting systems. In the phylogenetic evolution of species the development of vision has kept pace with the development of motility. Man is a "space-eater" because he has "distance receptors." The eyes give us information about the physical objects upon which our motor organs must act. In pragmatic terms, perception is seeing a thing in such a way as to make use of it. Biologically it would be of no advantage to an organism to be able to see things, like molecules, which it could not respond to tactually or kinæsthetically.

Thus far we have not emphasized the point that one of the consequences of the evolution of vision has been to exaggerate the sharpness of outlines (contours) of bodies, though we have indicated that we do not have any sense organs to perceive the circumambient electric and magnetic fields of force surrounding all bodies and providing the "binding forces" of matter, microscopic and macroscopic. But—to anticipate—later it will be suggested that certain problems of science, such as the problem of the interaction of force and matter and soul and body, take their origin in this very fact that vision emphasizes the corpuscular nature of matter, or sharpens the "meniscus" between "matter" and its fields of energy. That is to say, since sight is "anticipative touch," and tactual perceptions, in their development, involve a synthesis of visual and motor space, both the senses and the musculature have conspired with the brain to mislead us conceptually. Thus the intellectual distinction between matter and energy, or particles and waves, may be a result of the fact that the eye, the organ of vision, is a direct outgrowth of the brain, the organ of thought. In this connection it is interesting to note that the quantum puzzle is being solved not only by thinking of light in corpuscular terms, but also by thinking of matter in undulatory terms. Generalizing this, we may say that the problems in some branches of science are yielding to solution by unlearning some of the cerebral reactions, or ideas, which have developed around sense experience. Perhaps when we have become accustomed to Schrödinger's notion of substance as a set of wave-patterns, the idea of matter as something eternally and absolutely distinguished from "empty" space will be relegated to the science of cultural palæontology as one of the fossils of human thought.

In subsequent pages we will assume that our interpretations of nature are to a large extent based on visual experience. The importance of vision in the physical orientation of man to his terrestrial and cosmic environment is generally recognized. Whether it is atoms or stars with which we are concerned—or cabbages and kings—our knowledge of them is made possible by sight, *and inferences therefrom*. When, for example, the astronomer labels a red star a relatively cool star, he is merely demonstrating the truth of the statement made in the thirteenth century by Roger Bacon, who states that vision alone tells us of the existence of heavenly bodies. Quoting Bacon's [6] own words:

. . . I now wish to discuss some principles which belong to optics. If the consideration just mentioned [the wisdom of the sciences] is noble and pleasing, the one in hand is far nobler and more pleasing, since we take special delight in vision, and light and color have an especial beauty beyond all things that are brought to our senses, and not only does beauty shine forth, but advantage and greater necessity appear. For Aristotle says in the first book of Metaphysics that vision alone reveals the differences of things; since by means of it we search out experimental knowledge of all things that are in heaven and in the earth.

The point which Aristotle and Bacon here make is beyond dispute. And yet the equally central importance of vision in man's *ideational* orientation to nature is not so obvious. What significance does the evolution of the visual apparatus as a physical instrument of adaptation have for the formulation of scientific and philosophical theories of reality? Is the evolution of vision a unique phenomenon in biological evolution? Is there any relation between the evolution of vision and visions of evolution? In brief, does the pattern of organic evolution bear any relation to the pattern of cosmic evolution? That there must at least be some interaction between physical vision and intellectual vision is evident when we note the extent to which visual imagery enters into the formulation of scientific doctrines. For example, explanation in science is frequently supposed to consist in drawing pictorial representations of the phenomena to be understood. It is only recently that some scientists have given up the hope of framing pictorial models of the

[6] In the section of Optical Science in the *Opus Majus,* translation by Prof. R. E. Burke, Vol. II, p. 419.

events and realities of nature. But to return to our fore-going questions: the answers to these problems can only be given after we have surveyed the relevant facts bearing on the matter, and we first turn to a brief statement of the rôle of light in vision.

VI. THE GAMUT OF LIGHT

Nowhere has the analogy between knowledge and light been so beautifully set forth as in the sixth book of Plato's *Republic*. Here we are told that three things are necessary to vision: (*a*) the organ by which we see, of which Plato says that it is "by far the most costly and complex piece of workmanship which the artificer of the senses ever contrived"; (*b*) the bond which links the source of light and the eye—this medium is light, and, as Plato puts it, "light is no ignoble thing"; (*c*) the sun, which Plato describes as a deity, the effluences from which is the author of sight. The soul is like the eye: it sees those things which are illuminated. Here we have the analogy of two ruling powers—one set in the intellectual world, the other in the visible. Plato here means that the sun is to visible things as intelligence is to knowledge. Unfortunately we cannot pursue this analogy, but must follow the journey of the gleam of light which carries its messages from stars and atoms to our brains.

Light brings us the news of the universe, as Sir William Bragg [7] says. However, the light we see is but a small segment of the total span of radiant energy which wings its way through our universe. The physicist tells us that the total span of radiant energy extends from the longest Hertzian waves used in radio broadcasting (hundreds of meters in length) to the very shortest cos-

[7] *The Universe of Light*, 1933, p. 1.

mic rays recently investigated so intensively by Professor R. A. Millikan and others. Lying between these extreme limits are the various types of frequencies given in Fig. 1.

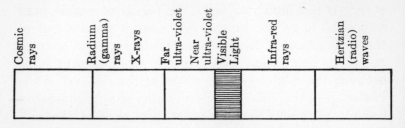

Type of Radiation	Approximate Range of Wave-lengths
Hertzian waves	40 kilometers to a few centimeters
Infra-red rays	A few millimeters to 8,000 A
Visible spectrum	8,000 to 4,000 A
Near ultra-violet	4,000 to 3,000 A
Middle ultra-violet	3,000 to 1,000 A
Far ultra-violet	2,000 to 1,000 A
Soft X-rays	100 to 1 A
Medium and hard X-rays	0·2 to 0·5 A
Gamma rays from radium	0·2 to 0·001 A
Cosmic rays	0·0005 to 0·0003 A

1A = 1 Angstrom unit = one hundred-millionth of 1 cm.
     $= 10^{-8}$ cm.
1μ = $\frac{1}{1000}$ millimeter.
1μμ = $\frac{\mu}{1000}$ = 10 A.

FIG. 1.

In discussing these "rays" we can refer either to their *wave-length* or *frequency*, which are related in an inverse manner to each other. Looking at the chart, it will be seen that, lying between the extreme limits, are the various types of frequencies, and, passing from the long to the shorter wave-lengths, we have the infra-red (or heat) rays, the visible spectrum, the ultra-violet rays, X-rays, gamma rays from radio-active substances, and eventually the cosmic rays, though in connection with the latter it must be remembered that some authorities claim that these are really corpuscles rather than waves. It is obvious that, even though the spectrum of radiant energy is not drawn to scale, the region of visible light responded to by the human eye is but a small sector of the total gamut of frequencies. Out of the total span of radiations the human eye responds to those rays lying between the relatively long waves at the red end of the visible spectrum (about 800 millionths of a millimeter in wave-length) and the relatively short rays at the violet end (about 400 millionths of a millimeter in wavelength). *Thus the eye, efficient as it is within those limits of the visible spectrum, is capable of responding to but one octave out of a total span of over sixty such octaves of radiation.* And yet what a tremendously valuable band this is to man in his attempts at perceiving, understanding and mastering his cosmic environment!

It is commonly known that what we call daylight is physically not the simple thing which it appears to us psychologically to be. The light from the sun is composed of the various rays we have been discussing. Unlike the auditory system, which can analyze a complex sound into its components (*fundamental* and *overtones*), the optical system cannot analyze the complex lights which constitute daylight into the monochromatic constituents. A prism, however, can do this, and the results are what everyone is familiar with, as portrayed in Fig. 2.

One of the interesting questions which arises out of a study of the facts presented above is this: Is it not a strange fact that while ultra-violet rays are physiologically more active than visible rays (being responsible, for example, for sunburn and the prevention of rickets) the human eye is nevertheless not adapted to function in this region of the spectrum? Similarly, that while heat (infra-red) rays stimulate our temperature sense, our eyes are not capable of responding to heat radiations? Why is the eye so highly specialized as a detector?

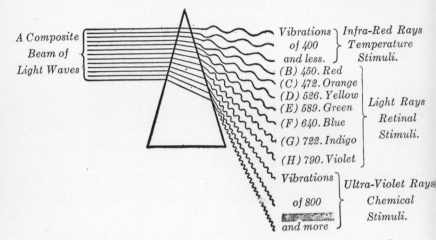

The prism's analysis of a composite bundle of rays of different vibration frequencies. On the right is shown the relation of vibration frequency to temperature stimuli of heat and cold, to light stimuli of the various colors of the spectrum, and to chemical stimuli. The frequencies are in million millions per second, as given by Wundt. The letters B-H are the nearest lines of the solar spectrum to the vibration frequencies selected for the standard colors.

FIG. 2.

The fact is that even for visible light the retina is not equally sensitive to all types of rays. This differential sensitivity of the retina is summed up in what the psychologist calls the *luminosity* curve, which is presented in Fig. 3. For the moment the reader should disregard the three stages in the evolution of vision as they are represented on this curve.

A study of this curve shows that the average light-

adapted eye sees best in the middle region of the spectrum, about the yellow-green (550 mμ), and will not
respond to infra-red or ultra-violet radiation, no matter
how great the intensity may be.

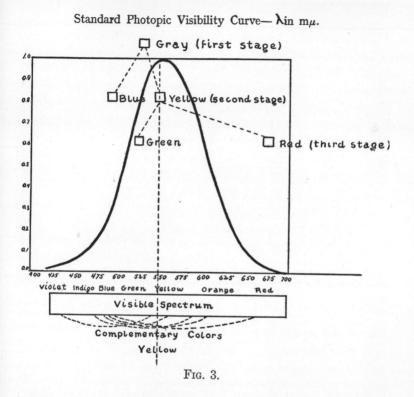

FIG. 3.

This, however, has not always been the case. Biologists
and psychologists know that the eye, like other organs
of the body, has undergone an evolution. This means that
other species of animals do not have the same type of
visual experience which *normal* human beings have. We
stress the word "normal," because not all human beings
have full color vision. Partial and total color blindness

are supposed by some to be a kind of atavism—a reversion to a more primitive level of response. And this brings us to the point where it is necessary to pause in our exposition and briefly survey this evolutionary advance of visual experience.

VII. THE EVOLUTION OF THE EYE

The great Helmholtz once declared that if his mechanic were to bring him an instrument so imperfect as the human eye, he would send it back to the laboratory for further improvements. It is difficult to believe that any scientist could take such a stand, for, next to the brain itself, the eye is the finest instrument the artificer of the senses ever contrived, as even Plato saw. To be sure, physicists now make photo-electric eyes, but no scientist could ever invent an instrument which serves *all* the functions of the eye so perfectly. And it is possible in a measure to understand how nature produced such an organ only by keeping constantly in mind the fact that it required millions of years to produce this instrument.

The human eye, a very recent addition to the biological world, is on the whole a more efficient instrument than the eyes of more primitive organisms. The general evolution of vision in the direction of improvement has carried with it the development of certain higher psychic faculties of great significance. To illustrate what vision at its best can be, let us enumerate the actual functions which vision now serves in man, having in mind perceptual and not conceptual functions. The following seem to cover all the functions of the eye:

(1) *To respond to light according to its intensity or brightness.*

(2) *To respond to light according to the direction of its source.*

(3) *To respond to light patterns; that is, to respond to definite images or shapes, which can then be transmitted to the brain.*

(4) *To respond to distance, or a third dimension, through eye-movements of convergence and accommodation.*

(5) *To transmit the color qualities associated with the objects in the external world.*

Roughly these functions are stated in the order of phylogenetic development; that is, the ability to respond to brightness was evolved first; later, when organisms with lenses and retinæ appeared, perception of distinct images was added; and finally the ability to respond to colors was achieved. In rare cases of progressive disturbance of function these capacities disappear in the reverse order of acquisition: chromatic function goes first and response to light intensity goes last.

The story of the evolution of the visual organs is not fully known, but even in its present fragmentary form it is fascinating. The beginning of the story dates back ages ago, when the earth had cooled down sufficiently so that life could take its origin in the tepid waters. We may obtain some idea of how the first simple organisms may have originated in the sea from the studies on the formation of formaldehyde and the sugars by the action of light of short wave-length (ultra-violet) on carbon dioxide and water. The irritability of living matter, which is a property of the complex and unstable carbon compounds, is the basis of the stimulus-response relationship. Since light of too much intensity is harmful to protoplasm, the surface of most animals was next protected by some sort of cuticle or shell from excessive stimulation, thus also keeping the light from the underlying parts.

Because of this general and diffuse sensitivity to light, it may be said that the lowliest of organisms are all eyes, for, as in the ameba, every part of the skin is light-sensitive. Even in some organisms more complex than the Protozoa the surface of the body still retains these light-sensitive cells, so that they can perceive differences in intensity, and even direction, of light. Thus a frog, deprived of its eyes, can still orient itself with respect to a ray of light.

According to some authorities,[8] the eye spot of the mollusk, *Solen,* is probably the simplest true visual organ that has a demonstrable structure. These same writers tell us that the eyes of some starfish furnish still other examples of very primitive light-perceiving organs, while the eye of the planarian worm furnishes an example of an eye of somewhat greater complexity than the starfish and Solen. Eyes possessing lenses and a retina, making possible the perception of distinct images, appear among the medusæ.

When we come to the insects we find that there are two kinds of eyes, simple and compound. The compound eye of a common house-fly is made up of several thousand eye-units, conveying a mosaic over the nervous system that must be very complex. It is a curious fact that some simple animals have quite complex eyes, while some highly developed organisms will occasionally possess relatively simple eyes. And in some cases both types of eyes exist in the same animal.

It is only when we come to the mammalian eye that we find an organ which is truly efficient,—especially in the primates, such as monkeys, apes and men. Not only is the vertebrate eye complex in structure, but its deriva-

---

[8] *A Text-Book of the Principles of Animal Histology,* by U. Dahlgren and W. E. Kepner, pp. 224-258.

tion embryologically is unique. All the primates have strong focusing muscles, and this is necessary to stereoscopic vision. The extreme complexity of the retina, which after all is only a part of the eye, is illustrated in Fig. 4; this shows the positions of the various layers of retinal elements—rods, cones, etc.

Plan of retinal neurons. (After Cajal.)

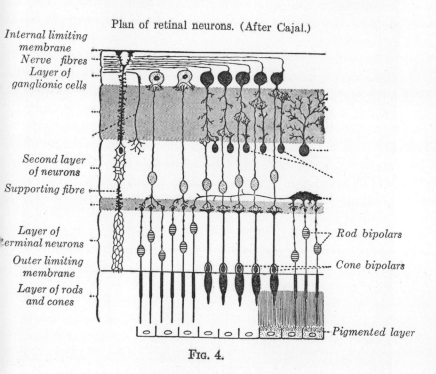

Internal limiting membrane
Nerve fibres
Layer of ganglionic cells

Second layer of neurons
Supporting fibre

Layer of terminal neurons
Outer limiting membrane
Layer of rods and cones

Rod bipolars
Cone bipolars

Pigmented layer

FIG. 4.

In going through the literature it appears that the one investigator who has recognized most fully the way in which the development of vision has kept pace with the evolutionary elaboration of man's higher psychic functions is G. Elliot Smith.[9] We cannot reproduce his argu-

[9] See his essay, "The Human Brain," *Nature*, 1924, pp. 390-393, and his book, *Human History*.

ment here, but will carry his thesis one step further. A
significant feature of vision in man is that the two eyes
do not contribute equally to the formation of a single

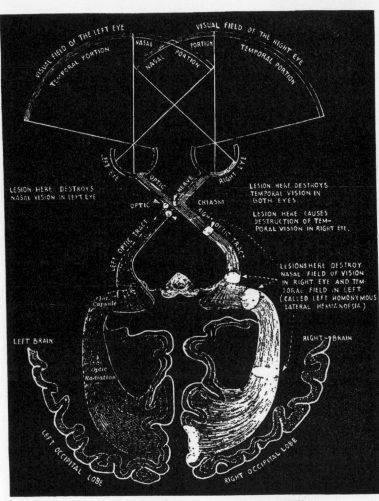

THE VISUAL FIELDS OF BOTH EYES

FIG. 5.

image, for in a right-handed person the right eye contributes more, and the left eye less, of the retinal picture.
The reasons for this are made clear in Fig. 5.

Eye-dominance, like right- and left-handedness, seems
to be a very recent evolutionary development, and it is
this which provides at least a modicum of fact for the
supposition that perhaps the seat of consciousness in a
right-handed person is in the left cerebral cortex, while
in a left-handed person the right half of the brain is
dominant. However, this is speculative, and we need to
keep in mind the fact that investigators like Bianci and
Troland [10] are more inclined to favor the frontal lobes
and the prefrontal association areas as the "seat" of
consciousness.

VIII. The Visibility Curve

The foregoing survey of visual evolution makes it clear
that lower animals are undoubtedly deprived of some of
the visual experiences which enrich the conscious experience of the human race. As previously stated, however,
not all human beings see all the colors of the rainbow.
Such persons are either partially or totally color blind.
In the Ladd-Franklin theory of the evolution of color
vision it is supposed that these exceptional individuals
(about two per cent of the population) are reverting
back to more primitive stages of visual response, where,
as is brought out in Fig. 3, such colors as red and green
(the *second* stage in the evolution of *color* vision, according to Mrs. Ladd-Franklin), or even yellow and blue
(the *first* stage in the evolutionary development of color
response), are not perceived. In some lower animals
these deficiencies of vision in the region of humanly vis-

[10] See L. T. Troland's treatise, *Psychobiology*, Vol. iii, pp. 54-55.

ible light are probably compensated for by vision in other regions of the spectrum of radiations, where the human retina does not respond. It has been asserted, for example, that the eyes of mosquitoes respond to infra-red (heat) rays. Perhaps mosquitoes find their intended victims at night in the dark because they "see" the heat rays given off by the human body. In that case the thermal "halo" or "aura" surrounding human beings is "luminous" to some insects, though invisible to us. Here is one way in which human vision accentuates the sharpness of outlines of bodies.

It will be observed that the above conclusion does not exclude the possibility that under some conditions (not normal to us) vision in the infra-red region of the spectrum would be advantageous to humans. This would be true in foggy or smoky conditions. Photographically (with the use of the proper plates) the details of pictures take in fog, using infra-red rays rather than visible light, are much clearer than images on plates sensitive only to visible light. This fact has important applications in both terrestrial and astral photography, but the point for us to remember here is that organisms do not normally live in foggy atmosphere, and hence nature does not provide humans with infra-red visual equipment.

Looking now towards the other end of the spectrum, we find here that there are organisms that can "see" in the ultra-violet region in which the human retina again refuses to respond. The claim has been made that not only some fish, but even ants and small crustacea, may be able to see in the ultra-violet. Here again we see that the limitations of human vision serve the purpose of accentuating the contours of bodies, for there are some bodies emitting ultra-violet rays (e.g., mercury; growing onions and perhaps even blood, nerves, etc., according to Gurwitch's theory of "mitogenetic" rays), which, could we but see them, would make these things "visible" to us in the "dark." Here again this view does not controvert the fact that students working with ultra-microscopes find that they can sometimes get better results (clear images) looking at very small objects if they use ultra-violet light; but human beings do not have to react to microscopic objects, and hence nature has not equipped them with eyes capable of seeing in the ultra-violet.[11]

In surveying the evolution of vision over the entire realm of living organisms, from the simplest to the most complex, it seems fair to conclude that this development must have progressed in the general direction of an increased efficiency of light perception. Thus the human eye is on the whole a more versatile instrument than the eye of an insect, even though such organisms may see in

[11] Another possible explanation of the absence of visibility in the ultra-violet regions is set forth in the following quotation from M. Lukiesh's book, *Ultraviolet Radiation* (p. 218):
"Woodruff believes that it is strange that the human being does not have a nerve apparatus to receive impressions from ultra-violet radiations intense enough to be harmful or useful and still too feeble to make their presence known by conversion into heat. He suggests that our remote ancestors evolved in dark cloudy regions where ultra-violet radiation existed only in small quantities. Hence no nerve-sense evolved as there was no need for it, but evolution later turned toward the development of protective pigment. Then it was too late to evolve by variation a new sense."
As an explanation this does not seem very satisfactory. Some lower animals are capable of seeing in the ultra-violet, which indicates that these rays were present long before man appeared. And there is no reason known at present why these rays should have been screened off while man was evolving. Recently an interesting theory has been put forth explaining the disappearance of some of the gigantic prehistoric animals by the supposition that a volcanic eruption filled the atmosphere with dust which shut off the penetration of the sun's ultra-violet radiation, so that these animals got rickets and could not hold their bodies erect or defend themselves against their smaller enemies, and hence were killed off! But this—if true—would involve only a temporary screening of these rays, which probably would not affect human vision. Nor can the fact that water absorbs ultra-violet light—there being fluid media in the eye which to some extent absorb ultra-violet light before it reaches the retina—be the explanation of the *shape* of the luminosity curve.

regions of the spectrum that are "dark" to us. And yet when we try to formulate just how we should state this increased efficiency, and go to the experts for the answer, we learn that it is difficult to define the precise nature of this supposed superiority. In a general way we may say that the human eye is superior because it enables us to gain a greater mastery over our physical environment. But—and here is an important point—*we have secured this mastery because the eye makes the very best use of that which is at our disposal to be utilized.* In other words, since it is obvious that sight would be impossible without light acting as the adequate stimulus, any attempt at proving that vision reaches its culmination in man involves a consideration of how the eye could best utilize the available energy of sunlight.

Man, the lord of creation, functions normally in the daylight. The human eye will therefore function most effectively in the sunlight if it is so equipped as to use to the best advantage the available energy of the sun's radiation. Now the position of maximum intensity of a star's radiation depends on the temperature of the star's surface. As astronomers point out [12] for low-temperature stars (red in color) the maximum is in the infra-red; for stars of intermediate temperature, such as our own sun, it is in the visible region; while for hotter stars the maximum intensity shifts into the ultra-violet. This idea of an organic connection between light and sight is clearly pointed out by Frederick Soddy,[13] as follows:

The surface temperature of the sun is estimated at about 6,000° C., and the maximum of energy emission at this temperature occurs in the yellow-green. It is probably by no

[12] See for example, "Invisible Starlight," by P. W. Merrill, *Science*, 1934, Vol. 79, p. 20.
[13] See his article on "Rays" in the *Encyclopedia Britannica*.

means mere coincidence that this is also the most vivid color, in the sense that light energy of this color is perceived by the eye in smaller amount than that of any other. Probably the eye has adapted itself through the ages to make the most of that which there is the most of in the sunlight.

If, in the course of time, the sun should cool down, vision might adapt itself accordingly, as Soddy indicates. In those days, as he says, "the people, if any were still alive, would see red most vividly. Our violet would have faded out and become ultra-violet, and our infra-red heat rays would become visible light." But, we might add, perhaps we will not have to rely upon the uncertain generosity of nature to produce this change in vision: perhaps the technique for the production of mutations by exposure to X-rays (or some other frequencies) will have been developed to the point where biologists can make eyes to order! Then, no doubt, the inhabitants of London and Pittsburgh will be the first to equip themselves with infra-red visual mechanisms!

The more technical way of putting this idea is to point out that there is a coincidence of the peak of the curve of the sun's radiation with the peak of the luminosity curve of the light-adapted eye (Fig. 3). Recently G. I. Pokrouski [14] stated that this coincidence is not with the direct light of the sun, but with the light *reflected* from objects in the environment, especially the green leaves of plants. But this does not upset the idea of the adaptation of vision to the sun's light; rather, it confirms it.

This fact that the brightest part of the spectrum of the sun's radiation coincides with the summit of the curve of visibility provided the occasion for a discussion

[14] "Über die Ursachen welche die Lichtempfindlichkeit des Auges als Function der Wellenlänge des Lichtes Bestimmen," *Physikalische Zeit.* 1928, Vol. 29, p. 269.

in *Nature,* the English scientific weekly. From inferences drawn from a study of Professor Woods' photographs taken in the infra-red and ultra-violet light, Mr. T. Smith [15] concludes that the extension of vision into the longer and shorter wave-lengths would be attended by a loss of sharpness of visual images. Both Sir John Parsons, an expert in visual science, and Mr. Smith agree that *vision is now so constituted in human beings as to bring out as clearly as possible the sharpness of contours of bodies.* This conclusion, while important, is not entirely novel, since Bergson, for example, has argued that the geometrizing intellect atomizes matter for purposes of action. The present writer, taking the cue from Bergson, had also suggested the same interpretation of visual evolution [16] in these words: "In vision light has helped to build up the light-sensitive elements in the retina, and, on the whole, the evolution of vision has gone in the direction of providing a mechanism for the sharpening of the meniscus between matter and the field (of energy) so that bodies take on sharper outlines."

We are now prepared to answer, from one point of view, the question of why it is that the span of visible radiation is so narrow, or why the human eye responds to but one octave of radiation, and why the visibility curve tapers off towards the longer and shorter waves in the way it does. One answer is that if we saw more colors we would have to go outside the limits of the visible spectrum to find them (since the spectrum from red to violet is already filled with all the colors of the rainbow), and as we move outward from the middle, yellow-green, region towards the opposite ends of the visibility curve the amounts of radiation which reach the earth from the

[15] *Nature,* 1928, p. 242.
[16] Cf. the *Monist,* 1925, Vol. 35, p. 627.

sun become less and less. Another answer is that increased sensitivity in these extreme ends of the visibility curve would sacrifice the sharpness of images which
the human eye secures, which has hitherto been of advantage to the human organism in the struggle for existence. These two answers are entirely consistent with each
other.

But color vision, as we have seen, is only one of the
several functions served by the eye, and if we have regard
for the other functions of the visual apparatus it may
appear that there are other, though not necessarily conflicting, ways of stating the goal of visual evolution as it
reaches its culmination in the human organism. Let us
turn to these other considerations.

IX. The Limits of Human Vision

In order that we may see any object the image of that
object must make an effective impression upon the
retina. In order that this retinal pattern can be recorded
in consciousness certain minimal conditions must be fulfilled: (1) the light from the object must be differentiated from its background by a certain minimal amount;
(2) the light must cover a certain minimal area of the
retina; (3) the light must endure for a certain minimal
period of time. Thus there are three threshold values
which must be satisfied: (1) the *intensity threshold* of
the least brightness; (2) the *least size* (or visual angle)
threshold; and (3) the *time threshold.* While the laws
governing the inter-relations of these variables are not
fully worked out, certain approximate formulæ have
been proposed. Thus some investigators [17] have argued

[17] Cf. "The Action of Light on the Eye," by E. D. Adrian and R.
Mathews, *Journal of Physiology,* 1927, Vol. 64, 279-301.

that the response to light is constant, in the sense that it represents a constant product of *intensity* × *duration* × *area*. This means that within certain limits there is a reciprocal relation between the three of such a nature that if one (*e.g.*, brightness contrast) be diminished, the others must be increased in a certain proportion in order that the object may still be visible. Of course there is an absolute minimum below which we cannot go and still have a visual response. Thus the "limit of resolution" of the eye has been supposed to correspond to the least visual angle subtending one retinal cone in the center of the retina (the most sensitive spot). However, in dim light the minimal angle of the visual field must become correspondingly greater.[18]

In the foregoing account we have presupposed that we are dealing with ordinary sunlight, which is a complex of the separate monochromatic constituents which, as is seen in Fig. 2, the prism breaks up into distinct types of colors. But Fig. 3 indicates that if we are dealing, not with a complex of colors, but with rays of one wavelength (monochromatic light), the response of the retina varies; that is, some colors are more easily seen than others, with ultra-violet and infra-red rays being discriminated not at all. The question therefore arises of how our previous conclusions fit the facts when color vision complicates the problem. When white light is being perceived, the retina integrates the brightnesses of the monochromatic constituents into a total brightness, and the formula stands as stated; but since monochromatic rays in any given act of visual response have only one brightness, no such integration takes place. In this

[18] For a further statement of the experimental results and formulæ in this field consult the following books, *Seeing*, by M. Lukiesh and F. A. Moss, 1931, Ch. VII; and *Principles of Experimental Psychology*, by Henri Piéron, 1929, pp. 78 ff.

case the general rules must be modified in the light of the particular kind of color the retina is responding to. Since in this field the data about light (or photons) can be converted into terms of the quantum theory of energy, it is possible to discuss the facts in terms of the quantum laws of vision.

X. THE QUANTUM LAWS OF VISION

The fundamental unit of the four-dimensional world of relativity is termed *action*. In the quantum theory of energy this dimension is known as the *erg-second*—a unit of energy multiplied by the unit of time. It is interesting to note that quantum laws tell us that while the lights from different atoms (sodium, calcium, etc.) are of a different number of ergs, and the periods of a different number of seconds, the products of the two contain the same number of erg-seconds.

Light of shorter period of vibration (gamma rays, X-rays, ultra-violet light) contains the more intense energy. For this reason a small amount of high frequency light (violet) can produce results on a photographic plate which light of a lower frequency (red) cannot produce. It is for this reason that invisible light of high frequency is responsible for the photoelectric effect, as well as photochemical reactions. The quantum of energy for red light is 25×10^{-13} ergs; for violet light it is 50×10^{-13} ergs. (These may also be stated, respectively, as 2.5×10^{-12} and 5.0×10^{-12} ergs.) A study of these facts in relation to the time it takes to see the various kinds of light brings out the interesting fact that *the minimum amount of energy necessary to cause a visual response not only depends on the wave-length but also on the time of exposure.* That is to say, the response to any color requires time as well as frequency, and quantum theory shows that this unit of "action" to which the retinal elements respond (the *minimum visible*) is approximately the same for all colors. *Thus it appears as if vision had so evolved as to adapt itself to the minimum quantity of energy in existence.*

This conclusion is very significant. The fact that the retina is the most marvelous detector known is made evident when, using the Einstein equation for the energy necessary to cause the emission of an electron, we find that a single energy quantum (photon) for green light is adequate to excite vision. It is the applicability of just such principles which has led some investigators to formulate quantum theories of vision. Here we can refer to several such hypotheses.

One of the earliest attempts in this direction was made by Janet H. Clark.[19] In her view quantitative differences (*i.e.*, differences in brightness) are held to depend on the number of electrons emitted. Qualitative differences (in color) are said to depend on the velocity of the emitted electrons, in accordance with the principle that each wave-length causes the emission of electrons with characteristic velocity. Aside from the difficulty of equating the theoretical velocity of electron displacement with the known velocity of nervous transmission (about 125 meters per second), the conception of each illuminated retinal element as a condenser system connected to the brain through a number of spark-gaps (synapses) employs an analogy which many physiologists will not accept.

Another investigator, Professor J. Joly,[20] also utilizing

[19] "A Photo-electric Theory of Color Vision," *Journal of the Optical Society of America*, 1922, Vol. 6, 813-826.
[20] "A Quantum Theory of Vision," *American Journal of Physiological Optics*, 1922, Vol. III, 130-149.

the facts of photo-electric phenomena, developed a theory of vision which he hoped would explain all the facts of color vision. But this view fails to meet the requirement that *every theory of color vision involves not only a theory of the nature of the retinal process, but also implies (or should contain) a theory of nerve conduction and of cortical processes.*[21] In Joly's view nothing is said about the nature of nerve conduction. This same objection applies to the more recent theory presented by W. M. Venable,[22] who focuses his attention on the retinal and optic nerve processes, without giving us any insight into the corresponding processes in the visual (occipital) cortex. That quantum phenomena apply to the cortical-conscious phases of sense perception may indeed be a fact, though none of the theories of vision thus far elaborated tells us anything about the details of such processes.

XI. PSYCHOLOGICAL RELATIVITY

In the previous sections we have dealt with the problem of reality, showing how our perceptions and ideas are dependent upon physical relativity of motion and biological relativity of structure. We now approach the third type of relativity which conditions our knowledge of the external world. In our study of the nature of psychological relativity we shall still be concerned with the problem of color vision, and in connection with this subject we shall have occasion to frame a few general suggestions about the possible mechanisms within the

[21] On this matter see the author's booklet, *The Alchemy of Light and Color*, 1928, p. 50.

[22] "The Quantum Theory and the Stimuli for the Visual Sensations," *American Journal of Physiological Optics*, 1925, Vol. VI, 403-415.

cerebral hemisphere which provide the physiological underpinning of psychic life.

The difficulty of the problems we are here approaching is without parallel anywhere in the domain of science. Thinking of sight alone, the existence of no less than eighty theories of color vision testifies to the complexity and the fascination of the problem. To indicate something of the mystery of vision let me present two quotations from several authorities who have studied this matter. Thus, in a recent book, Professor Hermann Weyl [23] traces the relation between the external object and the retinal pattern, and then continues:

The processes on the retina produce excitations which are conducted to the brain in the optic nerves, maybe in the form of electric currents. But between the physical processes which are released in the terminal organ of the nervous conductors in the central brain and the image which thereupon appears to the perceiving subject, there gapes a hiatus, an abyss which no realistic conception of the world can span. It is the transition from the world of being to the world of the appearing image or of consciousness. Here we touch the enigmatic twofold nature of the ego, namely that I am both: on the one hand a real individual which performs real psychical acts, the dark, striving and erring human being that is cast out into the world and its individual fate; on the other hand light which beholds itself, intuitive vision, in whose consciousness that is pregnant with images and that endows with meaning, the world opens up. Only in this "meeting" of consciousness and being both exist, the world and I.

The other writer from whom I shall quote is the late L. T. Troland,[24] who is also concerned with the transition from the brain to consciousness:

[23] *Mind and Nature*, 1934, p. 19.
[24] "The Optics of the Nervous System," *American Journal of Physiological Optics*, 1924, Vol. V, p. 151.

Here we encounter the greatest of the mysteries which exist in an attempt to understand "the optics of the nervous system." Eventually, we shall be able to trace the nerve currents through their successive transformations, not only from retina to calcarine fissure, but from the latter to the immediate determinant of the visual consciousness; and we shall be able to account for all these transformations in purely physical terms, as steps in a physically continuous process. But the step from the highest brain image to consciousness is not a transformation; it is a transmutation, accomplished by an alchemy unknown to physics. Here we are led to ask whether we should not add to optics, geometrical, physical, and physiological, a further inquiry: a *philosophical* optics.

The recent address of Professor J. B. S. Haldane before the Edinburgh Royal Medical Society, in which he presented an alternative to such conventional theories of vision as the Young-Helmholtz theory, again brings to the front this ever-baffling problem of the relation of consciousness to the brain. Professor Haldane here argues that there is no merely objective cause of color or brightness. In the present section it is our purpose to point out that we might admit this, or go even further and assert that it is sometimes the "mind" which creates the color effects it "sees," and yet still hope to find a definite physiological basis for the subjective effects that appear.

In general the classes of evidence for regarding color as a higher psychic phenomenon are these: (1) The study of progressive degeneration of visual functions shows that while *brightness* may be a function of the thalamus and the midbrain, *form* and *color* perception are localized in the cortex. (2) In the case of prolonged illness loss of color vision may manifest itself, due, as one might argue, to the lack of sufficient "mental energy" to discriminate, or pay attention to, colors. (3) In hypnotized children "real" colors and "suggested" colors can be blended to form complementary colors. (4) The fact that when a distinct color is presented to each retina, the two colors may blend in consciousness has been construed by Professor William McDougall as proof of the dualistic theory that psychic fusion has no physiological parallel. (5) Eidetic psychology, as interpreted by E. R. Jaensch,[25] holds that such facts as "color constancy," "color transformation," etc. (p. 86), prove that experience does not start with pure sensations, as Helmholtz and Hering supposed, but with higher mental processes. For example, "red-sightedness" is sun-adaptation (p. 109), which is peculiar to the "integrate" type of individual. (6) And now the theory of Haldane, that the "blue" of the sky is subjective, due to a protective mechanism balancing the brilliant yellow rays of the sun.

The facts above set forth force upon us the conclusion that sensation is not a property of the physical stimulus alone; rather, the quality of a stimulus depends also on the organism, its biological constitution, history, and present psychological state. What we need to explain this relative psychophysiological state of the organism is a corresponding theory of biochemical or bioelectrical relativity in the brain processes. Some progress has already been made along these lines. Thus, to explain the relativity of sensations the gestalt psychologists have appealed to the concepts of physical chemistry. In trying to interpret psychophysiological phenomena in terms of physics (transposing phenomenal gestalten directly into the isomorphic physical structures), gestalt theory presupposes that the biochemical reactions in the brain resemble the reactions of dilute solutions, involving the migration of ions in accordance with electrolytic laws.

[25] *Eidetic Imagery*, 1930. See also p. 209 of this book.

By utilizing Nernst's theory of galvanic chains Wolfgang Köhler [26] points out that an electrochemical law of potential differences precisely analogous to Fechner's formula for the differences in intensity of visual sensations can be derived.

The relativity of sensations to a general psychobiological background is a necessity not only of theoretical psychology, but its actuality is established experimentally by the fact that the presence of cerebral action currents arises from a difference in potential at two points, and whether such a difference in potential will appear depends on where one electrode on the brain is with respect to the other. By carrying still further Köhler's line of thought, the writer [27] has tried to show that a possible chemical basis for these relative potential differences may lie in the oxidation-reduction rhythms (or redox-potentials) so well known in inorganic and organic reactions.

One possible way of striving for a view which will yield a synthesis of psychic and cortical processes would be by way of a general theory of harmonic analysis, enabling us to make use of the entire repertoire of rhythmic phenomena—wave trains, Doppler effects, tuning, summation tones, difference tones, fundamentals and overtones, interference patterns, etc. In such a scheme, in which cortical processes would be dealt with in terms of the numerical coefficients of the components of the corresponding Fourier's series, the brain appears as a harmonic analyzer. As is readily seen, in such a view extensive use is made of the notion of *frequency* or *periodicity*. But we already know that "frequencies" are not the exclusive property of tuning forks, for, by analogy, La-

[26] *Die physische Gestalten in Ruhe und in stationären Zustand,* 1920.
[27] "Time, Space and Gestalt," *Philosophy of Science,* 1934, Vol. I, 197-223.

pique's chronaxic theory of nerve conduction can be interpreted in terms of neuronic tuning. The merit of such a view is illustrated by the fact that one is thus prepared to explain certain facts of musical æsthetics. For example, in presenting unusual combinations of tones to an observer there is at first low fusion, but with repetition there is an increase of tonal fusion. In trying to explain this well known phenomenon the assumption was made [28] that where two neurones are excited at different frequencies, the common neurone into which they enter takes on first the frequency of the lower tone, then that of the upper tone, and then a multiple of the frequencies.

Just what the structures are which function in these part-processes which are thus supposed to be endowed with their own proper frequencies is not known. We have spoken of them as individual neurones, but this need not be the case. Other possibilities can be devised. Thus, in connection with the above theory of tonal fusion, the writer was much interested in finding the following striking analogy from the field of physical chemistry, which purports to explain some facts of spectral absorption. It is known [29] that the total energy of a molecule is made up of the electronic energy of the radiating electrons, the oscillatory energy of the atomic vibrations, and the energy of rotation of the molecules as a whole. Now for the next step: In investigating the frequencies of absorption bands for certain substances, Prof. E. C. C. Baly [30] claims to discover simple relations between molecular, intra-molecular, and atomic frequencies. He holds that in

[28] Cf. *The Alchemy of Light and Color,* p. 57.
[29] See the article, "Magnetism and the Structure of Some Simple and Complex Molecules," by D. W. Bose, *Philosophical Magazine,* 1928, Vol. 5, pp. 1048-1067.
[30] "Light Absorption and Fluorescence," *Philosophical Magazine,* 1920, Vol. 34; p. 565.

some cases the frequency of the molecule is a least common multiple of the frequencies of the atoms of which the molecule is composed. Now if we substitute a cell-group for Baly's molecule, and individual neurones for the atoms, we have precisely the above theory of tonal fusion!

This, however, does not exhaust the possible analogies. There is nothing to prevent the separate resonators from being chemical diffusion fields. And this takes on interest when we recall that colloidal systems exhibit rhythmic phenomena, and that a resonance between two periodical chemical reactions is possible in the sense that their mutual influences increase with the decreasing difference in their proper frequencies.

The first analogy has the advantage in making it easier to see how electric and magnetic fields may play a fundamental rôle in psychic synthesis. So far as I am aware, the only author who has stressed the importance of the electromagnetic field in cortical processes is L. T. Troland. It is a fact of introspective psychology that conscious elements "interpenetrate," as Bergson would say. Thus a sensation of light and a sound sensation may be simultaneously experienced together in consciousness, and yet, on the bodily side, the centers of these sensations are localized in disparate structural parts of the cortex. Now there are only two possible ways of explaining this experienced unity: either field-forces must underlie such unification, or we must fall back on the notion of a very rapid alteration of attention between the two sensations, made possible by an equally rapid intercommunication between brain areas by means of associational and commisural fibers. But as Troland [31] points out, there are only two possible means of securing dynamical unifica-

[31] *Psychobiology*, Vol. III, p. 46.

tion in space, viz., electrical and magnetic fields (or lines of force).

Another advantage of this view is that it provides a basis for the unity of qualitative experience—such as a color percept—which on the physical side is composed of a discrete aggregate of units behaving together. This idea that there are electrical field structures which make conscious processes (*gestaltsqualitäten*) unitary things is in accordance with Troland's view, for he points out (*op. cit.,* pp. 119-120) that *physical structures which are minute below a certain point yield qualitative rather than structural differences, on the psychical side, and that if a configuration of electromagnetic forces is sufficiently intense, or well integrated, the psychical parallel is not a pattern but a quality.* To this it may be added that if consciousness *is* related to field-forces of variable and shifting cortical potentials the irreversible, or unidirectional, character of consciousness is then due to the streaming of Faraday tubes of force which extend into space and stream through time into the future.

Addendum

In the foregoing pages we have applied the notion of frequency, tuning, and chronaxy to neural elements. Aside from the references already made to work in this field, the ideas of two other investigators need to be mentioned. In the first instance we refer to the work of Paul Weiss (cf. "Erregungsresonance und Erregungsspezifität," *Erg. d. Biologie,* vol. iii, 1928, pp. 1-151), who has proposed a theory of nervous excitation in terms of the principle of vibration resonance which provides an interpretation of the "all or none" law. In a later paper ("Neue experimentelle Beweise für das Resonanzprinzip der Nerventätigkeit," *Biologischer Zentralblatt,* 1930, pp. 357-373), Dr. Weiss makes some further suggestions concerning the neural basis of *quality.* In the second instance I have in mind the work of Johannes Lindworsky, who, in his book, *Theoretical Psychology* (Eng. trans., 1932, pp. 73 ff.), attempts to deduce the laws of psychophysical processes from the principles of tuning.

It is a curious fact that Bruno Petermann, in his book on *The Gestalt Theory and the Problem of Configuration,* has used Weiss's work in attempting to refute gestalt theory, whereas Lindworsky's use of the resonance principle is entirely consonant with gestalt formulation. For my own part I see no necessary conflict between Weiss's views (which are still in process of development) and gestalt theory, and Dr. Heinrich Klüver has informed me to the same effect.

CHAPTER V

LIGHT AS THE LINK BETWEEN LOGIC AND PHYSICS

I. Logic and Physics

As we have stated in Chapter III, modern science has developed into a situation in which its integrity is threatened by certain paradoxes (antinomies) which, unless they are abolished, will discredit science as an intellectual enterprise. In the main these problems are epistemological in nature, and their solution calls for the development of an adequate theory of the relation of our conceptual constructs to the physical universe in which these logical systems find their applications. As an illustration of the type of difficulty in science which we have in mind, consider the problem of reconciling the difference in time estimates of astronomers and geologists.

Geologists use the radioactive clock (based on the relative amounts of helium in the rocks undergoing radioactive transformations) to calculate the age of the earth. The general estimates of the earth's age place it at between a billion and a half and two billion years. But the astronomer's calculations of the age of the expanding universe indicate that the astrophysical universe is relatively young: in fact, we are told, the universe started to expand *after* the earth was formed. Thus we are left with the paradox of a universe that is younger than the stars and planets of which it is composed! In such a situation there is surely room for the suspicion that those who talk about the "age" of the "universe as a whole" are talking nonsense. And just as P. W. Bridgman sees the possible solution of the paradoxes of *Mengenlehre* in the application of the "operational" theory in mathematics,[1] so we might suggest that an operational definition of time would show that it is illegitimate to use the same term—"time"—in such widely different contexts as astronomy and geology provide. But to decide such questions calls for an excursion into the domain of epistemology.

The issues involved in any problem which overlaps the fields of ontology and epistemology are numerous and complex. One way of approaching a problem, the solution to which involves a discussion of the relation of the logic of thought to the logic of reality, is to present a point of view and then discuss the relevant problems in the light of this central thesis. This is the method we are here following, and our initial point of departure is taken from two classical theories, which mark out the extreme limits within which our own position must then fall.

Here are the two limiting positions which we will use as "markers," presented in the form of theses.

The Thesis of Idealism: the laws of physics and the phenomena of nature are deducible from the laws of mind, or the principles of epistemology.

The Thesis of Materialism: the phenomena of mind, the nature of reasoning, etc., are deducible from the nature of physical reality.

Let us now examine the strength and weakness of each of these points of view.

The *strength of idealism* lies in the centrality of rea-

[1] "A Physicist's Second Reaction to Mengenlehre," by P. W. Bridgman, *Scripta Mathematica*, 1934, Vol. II, 3-29.

son; that is, no point of view can be put forth except in terms of reason, which by initial predication of the idealist is "mental." Thus in seeking to refute a materialist the idealist can always argue that the logical processes by means of which a science of physical reality is created are just as fundamental and real as the physical processes which the behaviorist *conceives* to be the necessary and sufficient conditions for such thought processes.

The *strength of materialism* lies in the actual success, attested to by much of the history of science, of explaining the observed phenomena, apparently material in nature, in terms of the laws of the interactions of material particles, or masses, in space and time.

The *weakness of idealism* lies in the fact that progress in the natural sciences has not come through introspection, as presumably it should if the nature of the world is to be understood in terms of mind.

The *weakness of materialism* lies in the difficulty of showing how matter can generate out of itself spiritual and intellectual values, such as "truth" and "falsity," "good" and "bad," etc. This type of thinking—that the existence of "error," etc., necessitates a dualistic theory —seems to underlie the following argument from Eddington[2]: "If the brain contains a physical basis for the nonsense which it thinks, this must be some kind of configuration of the entities of physics—not precisely a chemical secretion, but not essentially different from that kind of product. It is as though when my brain says 7 times 8 are 56 its machinery is manufacturing sugar, but when it says 7 times 8 are 65 the machinery has gone wrong and produced chalk. But who says the machinery has gone wrong? As a physical machine the brain has acted according to the unbreakable laws of physics; so why stig-

[2] *The Nature of the Physical World,* by A. S. Eddington, 1928, p. 345.

matize its action? This discrimination of chemical products as good or evil has no parallel in chemistry. We
cannot assimilate laws of thought to natural laws; they
are laws which *ought* to be obeyed, not laws which *must*
be obeyed; and the physicist must accept laws of thought
before he accepts natural law. 'Ought' takes us outside
chemistry and physics."

Later I shall suggest the reply which is to be made to
Eddington's argument from the viewpoint of the present
doctrine.

The preceding statements, presenting the two types of
monisms which form the basis of two types of epistemology, raise the question of whether the laws of thought
are derived from the laws of physics, as materialism
must assert, or, contrariwise, whether the laws of physics
are special cases of the laws of epistemology, as idealism
implies. We are now in a position to raise the question of
whether these two points of view are exhaustive and mutually exclusive, or whether there is a *tertium quid,* or a
compromise doctrine incorporating some of the features
of our two limiting doctrines. This, we here maintain, is
indeed the case; and the compromise doctrine we have
in mind resembles in some respects the point of view of
dialectical materialism. This last doctrine, associated
with the name of Karl Marx, is usually thought of as an
economic theory rather than as an epistemological doctrine. For this, and other reasons, therefore, the term
emergent materialism may be more appropriate as a label
for the present doctrine. Hegel's dialectic, the prototype
of the dialectical materialism of Marx and Engels, was
based on a developmental philosophy; but in Hegel's
case the theory of evolution was idealistic rather than
materialistic, as in the case of the "economic" interpretation of history. If we reinterpret Hegel's view, that a

human judgment is nature becoming conscious of its own processes, in terms of emergent materialism, we then have a theory which will not clash with the results of natural science, as Hegelian idealism did, and which possesses in addition whatever merits attach to the theory of dialectical materialism. Thus in our own formulation we may accept the revision of the Hegelian theory as stated by Karl Marx [3] in these terms:

"My dialectic method is not only different from the Hegelian, but it is the direct opposite. To Hegel, the life-processes in the human brain, i.e., the process of thinking, which, under the name of 'the Idea,' he even transforms into an independent subject, is the demiurgos of the real world, and the real world is only the external phenomenal form of 'the Idea.' With me, on the contrary, the ideal is nothing else than the material world reflected by the human mind, and translated into forms of thought."

For Marx the key to the understanding of the historical process is "competition," but the fundamental concept in the present doctrine is embodied in the term "transcendence." Physical reality, no less than the mind itself, has the power of passing from the given, the *thesis*, to an *antithesis*, and then rising above both in a *synthesis* which transcends the opposition. We have already noted a physical example of this dialectical process at work in the modern electrical theory of matter, in the concept of opposites (electrons and protons) kept apart and held together in a state of equilibrium in a field of force. A somewhat similar version of the dialectical process is evidently intended when Haldane [4] argues that

[3] *Capital, A Critique of Political Economy,* Author's Preface (1873).
[4] "Quantum Mechanics as a Basis for Philosophy," by J. B. S. Haldane, *Philosophy of Science,* 1934, Vol. I, 78-98.

"the historical evolution of mind in material systems has actually been an overcoming of internal contradictions."

In presenting the present view in terms of contemporary *gestalt* theory the writer has pointed out that we can think of any entity, A (which is the *figure* cut out from the psychic continuum), but at that same psychological instant we cannot think of what is excluded, the *non-A* (the *ground* of the conceptual gestalt). Remembering that the A is an abstraction from its own physical environment (ground), and that it is richer in its nature and possibilities than a *definition by fixation* of that entity recognizes, we see that it is because this definition excludes as well as includes that we have difficulty in following in thought the passage from the A to the *non-A*. The distinction may be illustrated by the difference between a mathematical (dimensionless) *instant* and the psychological *present,* or actual "now." In mathematics the "present" is a cut in the mathematical continuum, dividing the one-dimensional time-line into past and future. But the psychical present does have breadth—it *endures,* sometimes for as much as several seconds. The "specious present" of experience is trans-temporal. Consciousness is time-spanning, thus:

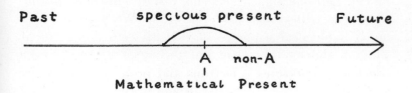

This power of consciousness to transcend the figure-ground, incorporating the thesis and the antithesis in a higher synthesis, in an act of consciousness which spans both poles is illustrated in the diagram, where the A is the mathematical present and the *non-A* is the negation of the present—the future.

This view of conceptual processes as logical gestalten with "boundaries" rests upon a doctrine of the relation of conceptual to perceptual processes which it is now pertinent to state in more detail.

II. Light and Sight

No one will deny that contemporary physical science is radically modifying our ideas about nature. When the implications of the new concepts which are emerging are worked out it will probably be found that the physical world can accommodate whatever factual basis there is to the "spiritual" realities which religion has postulated. We have argued that the new wave mechanics will turn out to be especially significant, for it promises to provide a basis for those facts of human personality which the believers of the dualistic theory of human nature have stressed. In the previous chapters we have engaged in speculations along this line, and the present chapter is a further venture in this direction. The doctrine as it now stands may be summarized as follows:

(1). Our knowledge of matter comes mainly through vision, and vision has so evolved as to sharpen the "meniscus" between matter and fields of energy. This conclusion is based on a study of the *visibility curve* of the light-adapted eye.

(2). The eye is an outgrowth of the brain, and the resulting visual reaction arcs are responsible for the sharpness of the conceptual patterns (as illustrated by the logical "law of excluded middle") associated with the sharp visual contours (as in the *figure-ground* boundaries) of sensory fields.

(3). The geometrizing intellect "atomizes" matter for purposes of action upon a world of external objects, as Bergson has shown.

(4). The relation between consciousness and the cortical processes of the brain is a special case of the general relation between fields of energy and matter. As stated elsewhere,[5] "the opposition between body and mind is paralleled on a lower level in the opposition between the corpuscular feature of the electron and the undulatory feature of the waves which show the electron where to go. In the human individual the transition from the objective (brain) to the subjective (consciousness) is a transition from the corpuscular to the undulatory, from the relatively discrete to the relatively continuous."

(5). In external perception we "see" the objects illuminated by radiation (light), but we do not "experience" that radiation as such.

(6). In internal perception we "experience" the energy-fields set up in the brain by the perception of the external world, but we do not "see" the matter of the brain which is the biological basis of this perception. Taking our cue from wave mechanics, we suggest that the best way to state the physical dualism underlying the mind-body relation is in terms of a resonance between electromagnetic tubes of force (Faraday) and the particles which are the foci of such energies.

(7). There is necessarily a similarity of logical structure between the brain patterns and the conscious gestalten. This "isomorphism" docs not require that the physical process underlying the thought of a differential equation be itself describable in terms of a differential equation, but only that there be some rule of transfor-

[5] "Relativity and Reality," *Monist,* 1931, Vol. 41, p. 530.

mation whereby mental processes can be translated into their corresponding cortical processes.

Let us now return to the further development of the epistemological implications of this view.

III. Light as the Link Between Logic and Physics

The reasons why the rôle of light in physics is analogous to the rôle of truth in logic are as follows:

(1). The analogy throws light upon the nature of the "logocentric predicament" in logic. The predicament comes about as follows: to reason about logic we must employ logic, but the logic we employ is not subject to criticism or investigation by itself. The parallel "luminocentric predicament" is this: to investigate nature we must employ light (radiation), but the light we employ cannot itself be investigated. This fact appears in one form in Heisenberg's principle of indeterminacy.

(2). In a world now thoroughly dominated by thoughts of relativity light appears as the only absolute left in the science of physics, a science formerly filled with absolutes. In Newtonian physics space, time and matter were "absolutes," but the constancy of the velocity of light is the only absolute which appears in relativity theory. That light plays the same rôle in physics which absolute truth does in logic may be made clearer by the following: Josiah Royce pointed out that *when we come to a proposition so fundamental that the denial of that proposition reaffirms it, we have absolute truth.* This principle appears in the work of Whitehead [6] and Russell in the form—*if not-p implies p, then p is true.* In terms of physics this means: *if the denial of light im-*

[6] *Principia Mathematica*, by A. N. Whitehead and B. A. W. Russell, Vol. 1, 1910, p. 108.

plies the existence of light, then light is a necessary con-
stituent of physical nature. That is:

(A) *Falsity implies truth, but the existence of truth does*
not necessarily imply falsity. This makes possible a
logical absolute.

(B) *Darkness implies light, but the reality of light does*
not necessarily imply darkness. This makes possible a
physical absolute.

(3). The *physical* dichotomy of (*a*) *particles* (or corpuscles) and (*b*) of *waves* (or undulations) is the physical basis of the *psychological* antithesis of (*a*) the *figure*
and (*b*) the *ground,* and the *logical* dualism (*a*) of *atomism* and (*b*) of *continuity.* Consider the members of the
first opposition:

(A). Light exhibits the properties of a discrete or corpuscular phenomenon, because it possesses mass and inertia, and cannot be a continuous process in a medium
(the ether of space) which does not exist.

(B). Light simulates the behavior of a phenomenon
occurring in a continuous medium, because it appears as
an undulatory process which is describable in terms of
the differential equations of hydrodynamics. Thus Maxwell's field equations for electromagnetism presuppose a
mathematics of continuous quantities.

(4). Light possesses the remarkable property of (*a*)
finiteness of velocity, while yet (*b*) exhibiting one of the
properties of the transfinite. The first property, (*a*), is
an experimental fact, as well as a necessary consequence
of the theory of relativity. The second property, (*b*), follows from the fact that just as an infinite aggregate is
that which can neither be increased nor decreased by addition or subtraction, so the velocity of light can neither
be increased nor decreased by any physical experiment.

As Professor H. T. Davis [7] says, "the transfinite cardinal, which measures the totality of rational points, is from one point of view identical with the denominate number which measures the velocity of light."

The further development of this epistemological theme might reveal how we may derive the logical structure of thought from the mathematical structure of light, and *vice versa.* In pursuing this investigation we would inevitably be faced with the proposal that modern physics compels us to reject the traditional "laws of thought." The writer [8] has already struggled with this issue, and proposed that we picture the present situation in terms of the Hegelian Dialectic, as follows:

THESIS: $\quad A = A \begin{cases} \textit{An electron is an electron (particle).} \\ \textit{Light is a wave motion (undulatory).} \end{cases}$
(*Law of Identity*)

ANTITHESIS: $\quad A \lessdot A \begin{cases} \textit{An electron is undulatory.} \\ \textit{Light is corpuscular.} \end{cases}$
(*Denial of Identity*)

SYNTHESIS: $\quad A = A$ and non-A $\begin{cases} \textit{Electrons are corpuscular} \\ \textit{and undulatory.} \\ \textit{Light is undulatory and} \\ \textit{corpuscular.} \end{cases}$

According to Hegel's view, evolution is the overcoming of contradiction. Undoubtedly Hegel would be pleased with the above pattern of development and would approve the statement of J. B. S. Haldane [9] that "our ideas about matter are subject to an internal contradiction, which shows itself in the uncertainty principle."

If we restate our own view in terms of the theory of emergent evolution, it comes to this: an electron loses its

[7] *The Philosophy of Modern Science*, 1931, p. 176.
[8] Cf. "Physics and the Laws of Thought," *Psyche*, 1931, Vol. 11, 70-80.
[9] "Quantum Mechanics as a Basis for Philosophy," *Philosophy of Science*, 1934, Vol. 1, p. 80.

identity in a material aggregate. What makes the aggregate is the wave system. There are no electrons in a universe devoid of waves any more than there are disembodied waves in a universe devoid of particles. This means that since waves (rhythms) are never isolated from all matter, it is the universe of matter which makes possible the emergence of rhythms; and it is the existence of rhythms, or repeating wave-patterns, which, at certain nodal points, gives rise to corpuscles. Thus the law of identity is the thesis which is negated in emergent evolution, when material particles lose their identity in larger wholes.

IV. Light as the Link Between Mind and Brain

The general thesis that light is the link between logic and physics carries with it as a corollary the doctrine that light furnishes also the nexus between consciousness and the brain. Aside from reasons previously given, the arguments in favor of this view may here be set forth under three heads.

(1). Light is the only reality which can provide the physical basis for that desideratum of philosophy—an epistemological monism. If we are to avoid the difficulties of a "copy" theory of truth, we must suppose that in the act of knowing the knower and the thing known are in some sense one, or in rapport. One physical theory which shows us how to get the brain, and the mind, in touch with external objects is wave mechanics. The wave aspect of matter makes this possible through a "resonance" between material systems. Previous to this idea, G. N. Lewis had already pointed out that in relativity geometry the eye, in visual perception, touches the star it sees almost as literally as my finger touches the table.

(2). Thinking goes on in terms of concepts, and concepts are the "atoms" of thought which are cut out from the background of the psychic continuum. In this respect the differentiation of ideas within a more general milieu resembles the articulation of the *figure* of gestalt theory within its own *ground*. This similarity is not accidental, since there is a close connection between the patterns of thought and the visual images of perception, as previously noted in the section on *light and sight*. The parallel becomes more convincing when we recall that the unconscious mental tendencies in thinking which the scientist follows involve psychological processes which, like visual perceptions, as Helmholtz has shown, contain a number of condensed reasonings. From this fact Émile Meyerson [10] has concluded that reason, like the eye, understands (sees) all else, but not itself. The reason for this logocentric predicament (the inability of reason to scrutinize itself), and the analogy of this to the luminocentric predicament have already been given.

(3). Another consequence of the general idea that the brain-consciousness antithesis is analogous to the particle-wave dualism is that in any thinking which involves a transition from atomism to continuity we must *experience* a difficulty which is the mental equivalent of the actual physical transition. Physics teaches us that waves and particles, and the transactions between them, exhibit both continuity and discreteness, so that we should expect a breakdown of the law of identity and the law of excluded middle in the physical basis of thought in the brain, no less than to the conscious processes associated with that transition. In other words, if the transition from the brain to consciousness *is* the transition from the particle aspect of matter to the wave aspect, and if the law of

[10] *Du Cheminenment de la Pensée.*

identity is inapplicable on the physical side, then it must also be inapplicable on the mental side when we try to think through this situation. What I am here trying to say is that we cannot logically explain this physical wave-particle, or mathematical continuity-atomism, opposition, because it violates the law of identity, and we cannot escape the laws of thought because our thinking, in the very thought-process of identification ("a corpuscle is a corpuscle"), is constrained by the physical structure of the brain in which the law of identity is for the moment observed. To be sure, we pass from one brain pattern ("A") to another ("non-A"), just as in consciousness we pass from one object of thought to another, which was previously ruled out from the focus of attention. Thus, as previously stated, the brain-mind transcends the particle-wave, figure-ground, opposition in a temporal process which achieves a higher synthesis; but it is precisely this transcendence which constitutes the *unthinkable* element.

V. VALUES: PHYSICAL OR SPIRITUAL?

In order that the present view may lay claim to superiority over the idealistic scheme it must dispose of the difficulty, previously stated, which Eddington has posed for materialism. The clue to the resolution of this difficulty lies in the recollection that the third movement of the dialectical process, the synthesis, is a creative process. In terms of emergent materialism this means that as a result of the interaction between a human organism and its environment a new set of relations arises which presents something new. Thus in social evolution *values* arise. What Eddington fails to realize is that "truth" is a social concept; it is a value. As such it has meaning only in connection with the reactions of human organisms functioning in a social environment. Its "frame of reference" is social, and not cortical. A quantum jump in an atom is neither true nor false, neither good nor bad; it just *is!* We should no more apply the notion of truth to the behavior of a single electron or atom than we would apply the concept of democracy to Robinson Crusoe.

The common conception of materialism, at any rate when it is generalized in the form of the "mechanistic" theory of living organisms and biological evolution, is that *structure determines function.* This means that from the observation of the structure of a system, and a knowledge of the laws of the behavior of the elementary constituents, the macroscopic behavior of that system can in all cases be predicted. But in the present theory of emergent materialism this is not necessarily the case, and this may constitute a differentiating characteristic between it and dialectical materialism. Bergson has supposed that mechanism means this: *same cause ⇆ same effect;* so that if you get the *same* effect by *different* means (*e.g.,* the presence of a visual organ in two unrelated species), mechanism is thereby refuted. Without raising the question of whether this view of Bergson constitutes a valid refutation of a mechanistic theory of evolution, it may be pointed out that the maxim, *structure determines function* (or *same cause ⇄ same effect*), is certainly open to question when, for example, in human beings the relation between brain states and thought processes is in question.

It is probably true that most materialisms have assumed a one-to-one correspondence between thought patterns and neural events, so that if one is known the other is in principle capable of being inferred. But in the present theory of emergent materialism the notion of a one-to-one correlation between conscious patterns and neural configurations is rejected in favor of a many-one type of correlation. On such a theory there is no single-valued correspondence between structure and function. After formulating this view the writer discovered that another investigator had hit upon the idea that the *same* brain state might be produced by *different* routes or histories. I refer here to Professor W. P. Montague, for, according to C. I. Lewis,[11] to explain "error" Professor Montague introduced a "theory of a plurality of causes which can produce the same brain-state, and explain error through the ambiguity thus introduced." This view, entirely consistent with our own conception, coupled with the previous remarks concerning the social nature of truth, and other values, should take care of the difficulty which bothers Professor Eddington.

[11] *Mind and the World Order,* 1929, p. 43.

CHAPTER VI

NATURALISM AND THE NEW PHYSICS

I. The Nature of "Mechanism"

THERE is something to be said for "isms" and much to be said against them. Against the use of "isms" in philosophy it may be pointed out that when philosophy thus becomes the "art of affixing labels" it degenerates into the give and take of refutations and counter-refutations between opposing points of view. But in favor of the development of "types" of philosophy it must be noted that to think systematically is to classify, to state one "ism" as opposed to another. And so those who, like the author in the present book, classify themselves as "naturalists" assume the obligation of stating the meaning and the implications of the term "nature."

According to my best understanding, "naturalism" gets its main significance from its opposition to "supernaturalism." Naturalism, therefore, may be defined as the doctrine that there are no phenomena or events in existence which do not fall within the domain of nature. If, for example, "God," or the "soul," are realities, they are inseparably bound up with the physical universe, in the same way, perhaps, that musical harmony and logical structure are dependent upon a physical basis. Let it be noted, however, that this does not mean that what historical materialism has described as the physical world is the whole of reality, for modern physics teaches us that the physical universe is much richer than the older materialism ever admitted.

In undertaking to show how modern science makes the older materialistic view impossible to maintain, it is necessary to state the meaning of the term, mechanistic materialism, as it will here be employed.

The classical statement of the mechanistic position was given by Laplace; since it has not been improved upon, it is here reproduced in Laplace's [1] own words:

We ought then to regard the present state of the universe as the effect of its anterior state and the cause of the one which is to follow. Given for one instant an intelligence which could comprehend all the forces by which nature is animated and the respective situation of the beings who compose it— an intelligence sufficiently vast to submit these data to analysis—it would embrace in the same formulas the movements of the greatest bodies of the universe and those of the lightest atom; for it nothing would be uncertain and the future, as the past, would be present to its eyes.

Laplace, because of his attainments in mathematics and science, was peculiarly fitted to summarize the essentials of this doctrine.

The presuppositions and general implications of this mechanistic doctrine appear to be as follows.

Science, in so far as it is mathematical, is the study of *functional* relationships in nature. In general such functional relations are symbolized thus: $y=f(x)$. In its most abstract form, science is concerned with the descriptions of motions, and the correlations of the various types of motions described. Now motion is a phenomenon involving *space* and *time;* for example, *velocity,* one of the simplest measures of change (motion), is the *ratio* of the space traversed to the time required for such motion.

[1] *Theorie Analytique des Probabilities,* Eng. trans., 1902, p. 3.

That is, $v=s/t$. One of the most important types of motion is that illustrated by the behavior of a body acted upon by a "force." Such a body undergoes *accelerated* motion: there is a change in the rate of velocity of the moving body. That is:

$$a = \frac{d^2\,s}{d\,t^2}$$

This is what is known as a differential equation.

The science of bodies acted upon by forces is called *dynamics,* and dynamics is especially concerned with conservative systems, *i.e.,* systems in which there is a *conservation* of motion (energy). Such systems are subject to treatment in terms of the infinitesimal calculus.[2] In the mechanistic universe of Laplace there is good reason why the equations of motion must be differential equations of the second order. It is necessary to satisfy this requirement in order that the description of nature does not contain explicit reference to time, for only thus is a physical system a causal and closed (conservative) one. Moreover, as de Sitter points out,[3] *inertia* is a fundamental fact of nature, to be accepted without explanation, and this "can be expressed in its most simple form by saying that it (inertia) requires the fundamental laws of nature to be differential equations of the second order." Thus, as in the above example of accelerated motion, the equations of motion of a conservative system are linear differential equations of the second order.

In such cases as we have been considering, time enters as the "independent variable," and this has the impor-

[2] These matters are discussed by V. F. Lenzen in his book, *The Nature of Physical Theory,* 1931, Ch. IV, and by Henry Margenau in an article on the "Meaning and Scientific Status of Causality," in the *Philosophy of Science,* 1934, Vol. I, 133-148.

[3] *Kosmos,* 1932, by William de Sitter, pages 107 and 109.

tant consequence that the solution holds just as well if the motion is reversed. Since it makes no difference whether "t" is *plus* or *minus*—the square of a negative quantity yields a positive quantity—there can be no difference in time between "forward" or "backward," so far as mechanism sees. It is this reversibility of time which provides the basis for Bergson's criticisms of the "mechanistic" conception of the universe.

Since the advent of Bergsonism, it has become customary to assert that a mechanical universe is one in which time does not count, because time, in physical science, plays the rôle of an independent variable. A strictly mechanical universe is one in which the processes can be reversed. All that can happen is the redistribution of mass particles in space; in Bergson's words, time becomes a "phantom" of space. This is the case, as noted above, in the differential equations where the second derivative is acceleration. From the mechanistic viewpoint this mathematical approach has the additional advantage that, in stating the laws of nature in terms of differential equations, the scientist converts the notion of "causation" into that of functional dependence, thereby eliminating the importance of the temporal interval, while at the same time reducing to a minimum the possibility that qualitative novelties may appear in the process of change. This point has been well made by P. W. Bridgman[4] when he tells us that those properties of a system which can be described in terms of linear differential equations have the property of *additivity*: the effect of a number of elements is the sum of the effects separately, and no new properties appear in the aggregate which were not present in the individual elements.

The theory of relativity does not, at least at first sight,

[4] *The Logic of Modern Physics,* 1927, p. 221.

appear to weaken the case for mechanism, since in the four-dimensional space-time manifold of the theory of relativity the space coördinates are tied up with time in one equation, and analytically such equations are dealt with in the same way as those of three-dimensional space; indeed, time can be turned into space merely by giving it a minus sign! This, presumably is what Minkowski means when he says that in relativity physics three-dimensional dynamics becomes four-dimensional statics. But in reality the theory of relativity *does* alter the mechanistic view, as I shall try to show.

Some of the opponents of the mechanistic view, Driesch, Bergson, *et al.*, have assumed that the only alternative to the view they wish to refute is vitalism. But the advocates of the doctrine of emergent evolution and gestalt psychology have also set forth the defects of the mechanistic theory, while trying to provide their own positive reconstruction. These two doctrines both recognize that in chemical and biological syntheses some properties are *additive* and some are *non-additive*. In order to clarify this distinction it is necessary to define more accurately what we mean by *linearity* or *additivity*. The following equation can be used as an illustration of linear functionality: $f(x+y) = f(x) + f(y)$. As is seen, this means that a function of the sum is here equal to the sum of functions. Such a relation holds in calculus when dealing with equations in which the "derivative of the sum is the sum of derivatives," and the "integral of the sum is the sum of integrals." In vector analysis, where the addition of vectors is defined by the familiar parallel of forces, we have an illustration of the kind of *resultant effects* which prevail in the mechanical universe of Laplace. As opposed to such additive effects, the emergent effects of non-summative wholes must also be considered.

When dealing with wholes (W), the properties of which are additive $(W\ add.)$, the result can be represented by a linear equation symbolized in the most general form as follows:

$$W\ add. = f(A) + f(B) + f(C)\ldots\ldots n.$$

But the properties of a true emergent, or gestalt, are non-additive; the properties of the whole $(W\ non\text{-}add.)$ are not the sum of the properties of the constituents, and mathematically we can only indicate:

$$W\ non\text{-}add. = f(A, B, C\ldots\ldots n)$$

In the very first instance in which the writer [5] accepted the theory of emergent evolution the importance of non-linear equations for organismic processes was set forth in these words: "The many chemical processes in a complex organism are not representable by straight line equations. Protoplasm is not a single, homogeneous substance. The orderly operation of cells results from the dynamic equilibria in a polyphasic colloidal system. Chemically life is not given as a linear equation, for the bi-molecular and tri-molecular reactions give equations of the second and third orders, and so on."

The thesis of the present chapter is that the same considerations apply in the non-biological sciences, though perhaps to a less extent than in the organic world. If this extension of an organic view to the wider world of nature is legitimate, then the following objections to the doctrine of mechanistic materialism make it impossible to maintain this view as a philosophy of nature.

[5] "Life as a Form of Chemical Behavior," *Monist*, 1924, Vol. 34, 150-160.

II. The Limitations of Mechanism

1. In a mechanical universe the future state is predictable from the present state because the properties of the universe are the sum of the properties of the parts of which the universe is composed. This is assumed by Laplace, and the mathematics of the situation is merely an extension of such arguments as are presented by Bridgman (though Bridgman, on "operational" grounds, might refuse to speak of the present or future "state of the universe"). On a mechanistic theory the properties of the universe as a whole must be additive, for only thus can time be reversible. But it is very doubtful whether, in actual fact, cosmic time *is* reversible. There are at least four difficulties to be overcome: (*a*) the exact form which the time and space (or space-time) coördinates shall take it still a moot question. Aside from the possibility that the cosmic time-line does not return upon itself, but is open towards plus and minus infinity, we have (*b*) the difficulty with the possible influence of the second law of thermodynamics, which, if cosmic extrapolation from observed systems be permissible, decrees an end to cosmic time someday. In this sense the universe may again be non-mechanical. Then again (*c*), the application of *geodesics* in the space-time manifold is an unsettled problem (related to the first difficulty), so that the precise form which the principle of conservation shall take is unsettled. As the writer [6] has stated: in ordinary mechanics the physicist "likes to picture the motion of bodies as a linear function between the coördinates of space and time. This is a straight line in the geometry of cartesian coördinates. The exact form which this demand that bodies move in minimal lines should take in the theory

[6] "A Spiritual Behaviorism," *Monist*, 1927, Vol. 37, 289-308.

of relativity is a matter of dispute. The problem is to translate the restriction that $\int ds$ be a minimum (*i.e.*, $\delta \int ds = 0$) in terms of the geodesics of the non-linear equations of the theory of relativity." Finally (*d*) as Count Korzybski [7] points out, since Einstein we have begun to realize that the simplest and easiest-to-solve linear equations are not structurally adequate. As he states (*op. cit.*, p. 612), when we come to the General Theory of Einstein we deal with equations that are non-linear. In all cases where the effect of *two* causes working together is *not* the *sum* of their effects separately, linear equations are inadequate. This appears in relativity theory when the theorem concerning the addition of vectors (compounding of velocities) is rejected. This parallels what gestalt theory holds, an analogy which, I believe, was first pointed out by George Humphrey. In commenting on this analogy the writer [8] expressed doubts as to its value, but it now seems that this judgment needs to be reconsidered.

2. In a mechanistic universe time is reversible, so that, given the present "state of the universe," the Laplacian calculator could predict what the past must have been, or what the future will be. There are several criticisms to be made of this view. The mechanist insists that if we knew *all* the causes (antecedents), we could predict all the effects (consequents), but this, at best, is a mere tautology, and, at worst, a verbal subterfuge, since in any case where such prediction is impossible (or unverified) it can always be said that this is so because we didn't know "all." Aside from the fact that "all" here may be meaningless, it must be remembered that, as Heisenberg has pointed out, the question of whether, from a

[7] *Science and Sanity: An Introduction to Non-Aristotelian Systems and General Semantics*, p. 265.

[8] "Gestalt Psychology and the Philosophy of Nature," *Philosophical Review*, 1930, Vol. 39, 556-572.

complete knowledge of the present we could predict the future does not arise, because a complete knowledge of the present is impossible.

3. Mechanism assumes the existence and possibility of studying "isolated" systems: a situation impossible of realization in actual practise. In biology this means that mechanism assumes the possibility of separating the internal from the external factors, and by controlling the variables discovering laws of correlation between changes of external conditions and internal responses. But we know, *e.g.*, that organic systems are subject to cosmic rays, gamma rays from radioactive substances in the earth, etc., which are, *e.g.*, disintegrating millions of atoms in the bodies of organisms each minute, producing various physiological effects.[9] Even where such interactions are known to be spoiling our "isolated" systems, we know also that the result is not the sum of the effects acting separately. Thus human behavior is not the additive resultant of the influences of "heredity" and "environment"; that is, $B \neq f(H) + f(E)$.

4. Mechanism assumes that it is possible at successive times to reproduce and study the "same" systems. At any given instant (t_0), the position of any system—organic or inorganic—in three-dimensional space is represented by the three coördinates (x, y, z) of the given frame of reference. That is, $P = f(x, y, z, t_0)$. If we have two such systems—two hydrogen atoms or two amebas—that are equivalent at that instant, mechanism assumes that, unless one of them is disturbed, they will still be equivalent when observed at some later instant of time.

[9] Thus, in the July, 1934, issue of the *Philosophy of Science* the writer proposes that there is a relation between the time-sense of the human organism and the rate of cosmical expansion. Along the same lines we have the suggestion of Dr. W. M. Malisoff that there is a connection between the gravitational constant and the velocity constants of chemical reactions.

Thus system A, at t_1, is the same as itself at t_0, and the same is true of system B. This means that if A and B are the same kinds of entities, then A at $t_0 + t_1 = B$ at $t_0 + t_1$. Prior to considerations of relativity and quantum theory , it was maintained by some, on doubtful grounds, that the reproduction of the same biological system is impossible, but now we have better grounds for holding that this postulate is impossible to satisfy. In the first place, the separation of the space-coördinates from the temporal dimension is artificial, because an organism is a space-time unity; and, secondly, since no two organisms ever have the same *history*, they can never be "identical."

Now let us glance at the implications of these ideas.

III. THE ORGANIC THEORY OF NATURE

Some scientists have looked forward to the laboratory synthesis of living matter. This is based on the assumption that by duplicating the conditions under which life is supposed to have originated it is possible to create an analogue to an organism. But to make an organism one would have to duplicate step by step, in point of time, the actual processes of nature, for the rate at which a thing is done is an integral part of the nature of an organic entity. In many cases the speeding up, or slowing down, of a process makes the end result of the system undergoing change quite different from what it would otherwise have been.

Mechanism explains the "present state" of the universe in terms of *chance*—the absence of intelligent design or a guiding force. This is interpreted to mean that if you give nature a sufficiently long time all possible combinations and permutations of elements will result.

But it is very doubtful whether there is time enough for this to occur, since it is possible for a finite number of elements to enter into an infinite number of spatio-temporal configurations. How much time would be required to produce our present solar system, with its given population of plants and animals, on the assumption that it all happened by "chance," has never been computed, though mechanists have a tendency to assert that nature has already had an infinite time in which to accomplish her present results. The fact is, however, that the second law of thermodynamics does not give us an infinite time, either in the past or in the future. Moreover, if we are going to introduce the calculus of probabilities into the problem of purpose vs. mechanism, we must realize that if science teaches us anything, it is that the events of nature are not mutually independent and "equally probable," but mutually dependent. And how this should alter the calculations of time which nature requires for accomplishing her purposes we do not know.

The further implications of the present view have to do with the doctrine of emergent evolution. To bring this within the logical focus of our argument it is necessary first to look through a telescope and enlarge our perspective to cosmic dimensions.

The conception of the world to which we are being led by modern astronomy is that the universe is a cosmos possessing something of the unity of an organism. The figure of speech now most frequently employed to describe this world-egg is a bubble. The metaphorical pattern for this cosmic gestalt was originally suggested in the Rubaiyat, when the poet exclaims:

The Eternal Saki from that bowl has pour'd
Millions of Bubbles like us, and will pour.

Only now we need to substitute the macrocosm for the microcosm which Omar had in mind. If, however, the universe is an organism, a cosmic jelly-like plasm, or expanding-contracting universe of Abbé Lemâitre, in which the diameter varies with time, then the properties of the parts (island universes, galaxies, suns, planets, and organisms) must determine the character and behavior of the whole; and, conversely, the whole must determine the properties and behaviors of the parts. But this then presents us with a curious paradox, which Laplace, with his theory of the calculator who could predict the entire future of the universe, failed to take into account. The calculator of Laplace could predict the entire future of the universe from a knowledge of its "present state" (the terminology is Laplace's) because, on a mechanistic theory, nature is the additive resultant, or sum, of all its sub-systems. But, as we have just noted, such a view is not in harmony with contemporary speculations concerning the causal relation between the cosmic unit of action and the ultimate corpuscular unit of action; or Eddington's earlier idea that there might be some connection between the longest length in nature, the diameter of the cosmos, and the shortest length in nature, the radius of the electron; or his more recent idea that there is some causal connection between the rate of expansion of our cosmic bubble, the cosmical constant, and the total number of electrons in existence.

The antinomy we here have in mind, which seems to block the way to the acceptance of Laplace's mechanistic conception, grows out of the fact that the universe is analogous to an organism,—a space-time-matter cosmos in which each member of the cosmic trinity holds fertile intercourse with the other two. To understand this universe we must have a knowledge of the properties (actual and potential) of each end-term of the macrocosmic-microcosmic (stellar-atomic) antithesis; but, unfortunately, no matter where we start our investigation, we begin at the wrong end. We can't obtain a knowledge of the *whole* by *summations* from *inductions* based upon studies of the *parts,* because the behavior of the whole is not a linear sum of the functions of the parts; neither can we, by making *deductions* from *generalizations* about the *whole,* gain a knowledge of the nature of the *parts,* since this implies a prior knowledge of the universe as a whole which we do not in fact have.

These are some of the difficulties which a mechanistic theory of nature must face. If the present view is correct, those who are fighting for the validity of the mechanistic position are defending a lost cause. But the defeat of mechanistic philosophy does not carry to destruction the naturalist's position: nature is the whole of reality, and the supernatural has no causal efficacy in our pulsating universe of waves and particles. And when we think through what the "nature" is which the "naturalist" insists upon as constituting the "whole of reality," it may be found that there is "room" in this "physical" world for at least consciousness, perhaps also the "soul," and—who knows—even a "cosmic mind"!

CHAPTER VII

EMERGENCE AND FIELD PHYSICS

I. Emergent Evolution and Gestalt Theory

IF ONE were to formulate a general statement in the direction in which biological evolution has moved, the following formulæ might be proposed: (*a*) evolution has moved in such a direction as to produce organisms capable of dissipating a maximum of cosmic energy; (*b*) evolution has moved in such a direction as to produce organisms capable of reacting to the widest range and most complex purview of the external environment. These two statements are two different ways of summarizing the characteristics of that creature who by common human consent is the pinnacle and apex of the evolutionary process up to date—man himself.

In trying to understand the process by means of which this end result has been attained the writer has made use of the concepts of the "emergent evolution" theory. Interpreted in terms of this view,[1] the above formulæ for the evolutionary process may be restated in this fashion: the forward advance of nature results in the production of two different *types of order,* or *levels of simplicity.* We have (*a*) the first level of order, which is a *simple simplicity,* and (*b*) the second level of order, which is a *complex simplicity.* These two types of simplicity are illustrated, re-

[1] Cf. "Probability, Natural Law, and Emergence," *Journal of Philosophy,* 1926, Vol. 23, p. 430.

spectively, by (a) the simplicity of a gas, which is homogeneous and isotropic, and (b) the simplicity of a crystal, which is inhomogeneous and anisotropic.[2]

It is our thesis that *nature is never satisfied with the attainment of first level simplicities, but always moves on to the achievement of second level simplicities.*[3] It is precisely this fact which makes it possible for us to use up the stores of potential energy, which nature makes available, by seeking out and reacting to new stimuli. In other words, *through a period of time the complex (human) organism tends to react to the most complicated environment it can meaningfully simplify,* thus providing an outlet for the organismic energies. A psychological example of this reduction of potential energy to a minimum is found in vision in the *law of greatest horopter,* which, as the writer, following gestalt theory, has indicated,[4] is a biological application of the second law of thermodynamics, according to which potential energy tends towards a minimum (or entropy towards a maximum).

Our own theory of emergent evolution has been stated in terms of contemporary gestalt theory.[5] The two properties of a gestalt are, first, that as a *whole* the properties of the gestalt are something other than a linear summation of the properties of the constituent parts; and, secondly, the gestalt can be *transposed.* A gestalt is like a melody, in that it can be played in different "keys." Keeping these considerations in mind, I shall now try to

[2] I am indebted to Professor Kurt Koffka for this illustration.
[3] Cf. "A Phenomenological Interpretation of Physico-chemical Configurations and Conscious Structures," *Journal of Philosophy,* 1927, Vol. 24, p. 376.
[4] "Gestalt Psychology and the Philosophy of Nature," *Philosophical Review,* 1930, Vol. 39, 556-572.
[5] "The Logic of Gestalt Theory," *Psychol. Rev.,* 1931, Vol. 38, p. 365.

show that *gestalten* are related to the *field* properties as studied in physics.

II. EMERGENCE AND FIELD PHYSICS

In seeking for the explanation of the fact of emergence it appears that we must ascribe an important rôle to field forces. At least one necessary condition for emergence on any given "level" of nature is the influence of fields of force on the material constituents of that level. Gestalt theory recognizes this when it employs the notion of *attraction of forces* in the underlying brain processes to explain certain facts of phenomenal patterns. Thus two parts of the brain which are structurally distinct may, in terms of energy-coördinates, be functionally "closer" together than two other areas which are separated by a smaller spatial interval. Some experimental evidence for such a possibility is found in hydrodynamics, where a parallel for the attraction of forces is exhibited by the merging of two whirlpools of water through the properly timed opening and closing of two holes in the bottom of the trough of water. This analogue of Wertheimer's *phi-phenomenon* (the production of "seen" motion through a process of short-circuiting) has another parallel in electrodynamics in the attraction of two parallel conductors for each other when currents are flowing through them.

In our own interpretation we have postulated that every organic whole (atom, molecule, crystal, and protoplasmic system) carries with it a *field*, in the sense that the constituent particles function according to a unitary mode of behavior. In the case of a complex simplicity (organism), this rhythm is constituted of subordinate rhythms functioning within the unitary behavior plan of the body as a whole. Since, in the view as already presented, we have employed the term "ether" as a name for the fact that the behavior of the ensemble of discrete particles is ordered in time, we can say that every organism carries around with it its own "ether." This, however, is only a name for the fact of dynamic interaction between the parts and the whole.

There are at least three levels of organisms, namely, (a) atoms, (b) molecules, and (c) protoplasmic systems. In terms of the present view [6] the spatio-temporal unity of any organism is its mind. Now there is only one way of securing the dynamical unification in space and time exhibited in organisms, and that is through the influence of electric and magnetic fields of force. With this as a basis, we can suppose that the foregoing levels of organisms are generated from the following fields of force:

Electromagnetic field = *Atomic ether*
Molecular   field = *Chemical ether*
Gravitational   field = *Molar ether*
Mental   field = *Psychic ether*

This permits us to build up the following levels of nature:

Electrons — protons + *ether* = *Atoms*
Atoms   + *ether* = *Molecules*
Molecules   + *ether* = *Molar bodies*
Molar Bodies   + *ether* = *Mind*

In his treatise on *Valence and the Structure of Matter* (1923), Professor G. N. Lewis explains that it would not be very far from the truth to state that nearly every chemical process occurs in such a way as to increase the

[6] Cf. "Time, Space and Gestalt," *Philosophy of Science*, 1934, Vol. 1, 197-223.

net amount of conjugation. By conjugation is meant the partial neutralization of the molecular magnetic fields. The electrons of atoms conjugate to produce a couple which is self-contained magnetically, with little residual magnetic field. But—and here we proceed on our own— it is a fact that there are *residual* fields, and this suggests the general possibility that each of the above levels of force (atomic, chemical, molar and psychic) may be the aggregate of residual fields remaining unsaturated in the constituent systems out of which it emerges. That is to say, the atomic ether is composed of residual electron-proton fields, which maintain the nucleus and the valence electrons in an equilibrium; the molecular ether is composed of the residual atomic forces, which maintain two or more atoms in a unitary system; the molar ether is composed of residual molecular forces, which maintain molecules in unitary systems.

In a sense, each of these levels of organisms has a mind, or spatio-temporal unity, associated with its field of force. That emergence is somehow made possible by the presence of such an "ether" is the thesis I am here especially concerned to establish.

III. Waves as Phenomenal Patterns

One of the fundamental distinctions made in classical physics is the distinction between *matter* and *energy*, or *corpuscular* and *wave* phenomena. Such undulatory phenomena as light (radiation) were supposed to require some sort of continuous *medium* for their transmission. This appears in Maxwell's classical electromagnetic theory of light. Maxwell's famous equations, stated in terms of the calculus, and therefore emphasizing continuity, were devised to express the manner in which electromagnetic waves were propagated through the ether, or space free from matter. According to this view "matter" might appropriately be defined as the region in which Maxwell's equations do not hold; or a particle could even be defined as a hole in the ether. In either case the distinction between *substance* and *free space,* the arena of action and the seat of energy disturbances, was provided for.

As is generally known, the notion of the luminiferous ether was arrived at through reasoning by analogy, as follows:

water waves : *water* :: *light waves* : *ether*

The properties ascribed to the ether were also arrived at through reasoning by analogy. To see this one must consider the types of wave motions which occur in solids, liquids and gases. In *liquids* and *gases* (*e.g.,* water and air) only *longitudinal* waves occur. Pressure changes alone (*i.e.,* condensations and rarefactions) can be transmitted as wave motions. In *solid* bodies both longitudinal and *transverse* waves are possible. It is only in incompressable solids, in which volume dilation is impossible, that we find transversal waves, unaccompanied by longitudinal waves. The ether was accordingly conceived to be an *elastic solid,* because only thus could transverse waves alone be transmitted. Therefore on the older theory of light it was assumed that the ether possessed the *contradictory* properties of an elastic but frictionless solid.

This was one difficulty in the ether theory. Another arose in connection with the negative results of the well-known Michelson-Morley experiment. Thus the physicists were compelled to consider the possibility that there were "waves," without there being something (a medium) in which these undulations occur. This step was taken by Einstein in his theory of relativity, wherein the ether, as the hypothetical carrier of waves, is disregarded.

In more ways than one Einstein has done much to establish a corpuscular theory of nature in place of the older continuity picture. But even Einstein is not a thoroughgoing atomist—if indeed there really be such a person. The extreme position is seldom found, and this is perhaps due to the fact that no one would accept the logical and physical consequences of atomism pushed to its limits. One of the consequences of such an extreme position is this: the same type of argument which leads to the denial of light "waves" in a medium would logically lead to a denial of such presumably indubitable phenomena as "water waves" and "sound waves." In other words, the same logic which leads to a denial of the ether as a medium of undulation, leads to a denial of the existence of an acoustical medium or a hydrodynamical medium. A thorough going atomist, insisting that only particles are real, would be compelled to argue that there are no "media" in which wave motions can occur. Such an individual must therefore hold that *air*, as a continuous, fluid-like medium, is a logical fiction. The same is true of *water*, as a medium. An extreme atomist must argue that all that exist are the molecules of the various "gases" or "liquids" bumping together and making the "pressure." Detailed analysis shows that the "media" transmitting wave motions are composed of discrete particles. Therefore, the utter atomist should declare, the "wave" is a mathematical abstraction which is supposed to move along a kind of geometrical plane.

Mathematically a wave is a *function*—a relation between three variables of such a sort as to satisfy, in the simplest case, the following equation:

$$y = a \ sin \ (x - vt)$$

But what is the wave physically? For an extreme atomist, I suppose, the wave represents the averaging effect of the orderly displacement of particles. Perhaps even the *interference* effects of light, which seem to require an undulatory medium, may be understood as statistical effects, provided the statistical units can be assumed to be sufficiently small. As an illustration of the kind of view we are here referring to we may cite the intermittence theory of radiation presented by Sir J. J. Thomson.[7] Here Sir Joseph directs attention to the fact that just as a gas, which on an engineering scale seems to exert a continuous pressure, has a structure in time, the fineness of which is determined by the interval between collisions, so we may suppose that the electric field has a structure in time. In explaining the above types of waves (longitudinal and transverse) which exist in solids, liquids and gases, the differences in types of waves would probably be attributed to the properties of "media" as functions of the inter-molecular distances, the "mean free path" between the collisions of particles being greatest in gases, less in liquids, and least in solids. And so, to repeat, for an utter atomist only the discrete particles (light-quants, atoms, molecules of solids, liquids, and gases) are real, and the "wave" is a logical fiction or mathematical abstraction moving along a geometrical plane.

And now how shall we regard this position of the extreme atomist? For my part, I should agree that a theory

[7] *Nature*, 1926, p. 606 ff.

of waves based on averaging effects of statistical units is all to the good—provided we admit that molecular, atomic and electronic fields of force are active in the production of wave motions. It is the existence of these fields of force, associated with the material particles of the statistical ensemble, which "iron out" the discontinuities in the averaging process. Moreover, such wave patterns are valid instances of *gestalten,* or phenomenal patterns containing elements of novelty, and therefore are to be regarded as examples of emergents.

What would be the reaction of the extreme atomist to such a view? If atomism means materialism, then no doubt he would have none of this "mysticism" of emergence. Here, in stating this view, I have recourse to the summary of one of my former students, Mr. Eugene F. Coleman, who says: "To show how scientific formulation invalidates emergent effects, let us consider the case of a stretched cord, upon which a traveling wave can be set up by plucking it. The essence of the physical mechanism of such a wave is precisely equivalent to the case of waves on the surface of water; but I have selected the string example because the physical interpretation of the formulation is more clear-cut. In a string vibrating with small amplitude, the individual particles of the string have motion in only one direction: that perpendicular to the length of the string and in the plane in which the string is plucked. However, simple scientific reasoning based on the *Laws of Motion* enables us to derive an expression giving the precise distance, y, which any particle of the string is from its normal position, at any time, t, after any convenient zero of reference. This expression has the form,

$$y = p \cos (At - r),$$

where A is a constant, and p and r are simple stated functions of the distance, x, of the particle in question from one end of the string. Then, after the expressions for p and r in terms of x are introduced, we have a functional relation among x, y and t. This functional relation organizes the string in a unique way: we should say that a progressive wave passes along it. The wave is something new, a higher aggregate of organization, emerging from the more homogeneous background of the string-particle displacement. In some sort of vague way this wave may be supposed to have an element of complete novelty in it; but the novelty is, in principle, no greater than that involved when a particle is subject to two independent velocities in different directions and pursues a velocity in a new direction. In fact, the appearance of the wave is, technically, built up out of just such purely simple-combination effects as this. Any element of novelty which is present is something supplied by the imagination. Perhaps the full significance of this will be made clearer by considering that the wave is *completely predictable* in every detail by purely analytic methods—methods of the sort used in building up large-scale phenomena from the properties of small-scale things. If a mathematician who knew nothing of the waves on strings were given the bare mathematical relation between x, y and t, he could, without external assistance, evolve the necessity for the fact that aggregates of spatial configurations would pass along the string at a definite velocity. He would be able, further, to specify with complete exactness—that is, to predict—the amount and direction of this velocity, and the quantitative description of the moving configuration. In this sense there is no element of novelty, so that the case of 'waves' on the surface of the water (which is completely analogous to the illustration here used) does not prove that there is a 'creative' element in the 'emergence' of the pattern."

This is an excellent statement. Nevertheless, there is a subtle point which is overlooked in this reasoning, and that resides in the problem of how to get a continuous process out of the behavior of an aggregate of discrete units. And that is precisely what is meant by "emergence" in this case. In the instance of water waves no difference can be observed between the phenomena predicted on the basis of a mathematics of continuous quantities (infinitesimal calculus) and the empirically demonstrated facts. Here a large number of seemingly discontinuous elements (molecules) in an averaged state produce a plenum, the description of the behavior of which requires a dynamics of the continuous (hydrodynamics).

This reasoning applies to other instances of wave trains (undulations). The physicist tells us that the differential equation for the steady flow of heat, light, electric waves, and magnetism, where a is the velocity of transmission, is this:

$$\frac{\partial^2 y}{\partial t^2} - a^2 \frac{\partial^2 y}{\partial x^2} = o$$

This equation expresses the fact of *orderly* displacements in space, progressing along the time-axis. In all such cases, when the properties of the given differential equation are developed, the results are applicable to heat, light, etc. Thus the assumption is made that a mathematics of continuity is applicable, because we are here dealing with a *continuous* spreading out of energy from a source. It may be true that there is no interaction between the parts of a light wave, but if you are going to regard the light ray as a result of an averaging process operating in a statistical ensemble, there must be some dynamic interaction between the elements of that aggregate, and this must be due to overlapping fields of force. That waves may be treated as gestalten or wholes has in fact been suggested by Schrödinger.[8]

In the foregoing pages we have been discussing "emergence" entirely in terms of "waves." This is because we are here primarily interested in providing a basis for a theory of the psychic continuum as a function of a "mental ether," with its own functional and dynamic phenomena made possible by the force-fields associated with cerebral processes. But the same argument for "emergence" could be made in connection with any other physical or chemical properties which are a function, not of the elementary constituents of a medium, but of the behavior of the whole. Thus it is well known that the activities of organic colloids take place within fluid media, and it strengthens the case for emergence when we find phenomena which parallel "waves" as instances of emergent properties. Indeed the fact of the preponderance of water in organic phenomena makes it possible for a number of phenomena of great importance to occur. Among these we may list the following: (1) *surface tension phenomena;* (2) *interfacial forces;* (3) the *orientation of molecules* in liquid media; and (4) *catalytic* processes.

All of the foregoing, and other phenomena, are of superlative importance for the phenomena of life, and in the next sections it will be our problem to consider these processes as instances of relatively simple types of order (simple simplicities) which enter as constituent notes in

[8] *Die Naturwissenschaften,* 1926, Vol. 17, 486 ff.

the complex simplicity which is the larger rhythm of life.

IV. Physical Forces and Conscious Patterns

The full theory of liquids is not worked out, owing to the complicated nature of the forces involved between curiously shaped molecules in constant rotational and translational motion. The mathematics of such a process is complicated; and yet nature has worked out the solution to the problem of how to produce unity out of molecular chaos. As one illustration of this we have the phenomenon of *surface tension*. The most fundamental property of liquid surfaces is that of spontaneous diminution of area to a minimum. According to one explanation, this tendency to diminish surface area is due to the fact that the outer layer of molecules acts as a tight skin, tending to contract uniformly. Here a real physical meaning is ascribed to the "contractile skin" of the molecules of the surface. But according to another point of view the contraction is not due to a mysterious and hypothetical "skin," but is due to the presence of a definite amount of free energy in each square centimeter of the surface. That is to say, the terms "surface tension" and "free surface energy" are equivalent, and the surface "film" represents the net force of a unimolecular "surface," the attraction being perpendicular to the layer of molecules. It will be observed that this argument is similar to the one which arises between the "utter atomist" and the advocate of true waves, the "undulationist."

Here, as in the case of the "wave," we have a beautiful illustration of a gestalt. The surface tension of the film represents an averaging effect of the unbalanced inward molecular attractions. And yet it is doubtful whether one could predict *a priori*, from a knowledge of the behavior of individual molecules, the properties of films. For this reason the gestalters very properly take a soap bubble as an example of a non-summative configuration. Moreover, while the film or bubble, relative to its constituent molecules, is a new simplicity, these phenomenal emergents again appear in higher complexities, which, in turn, result in new simplicities.

Proceeding now to a discussion of *interfacial forces,* we must preface our remarks with the comment that physicists formerly attempted to explain the properties of matter in terms of a "generalized" molecule, which was pictured as spherical in form and surrounded by a symmetrical field of force. But this view, while satisfactory as a description of gas molecules, proved inadequate for the molecules of liquids. The newer view carries with it an abandonment of the idea that the molecules studied in chemistry are necessarily surrounded by symmetrical fields of force. Thus, according to present views, the electromagnetic field near a molecule varies greatly from point to point, and only at distances which, compared to the dimensions of the molecule itself, are great, does the field approximate one of spherical symmetry.

When we come to interfacial phenomena as they manifest themselves in biochemistry, the older view is of course inadequate. It is here necessary to picture the molecules of long chain (carbon) compounds as anything but spherical. Interfacial forces arise at the surfaces of contact of substances that do not mix together, or dissolve or absorb each other.[9] Such situations are present in the colloidal systems in the living organism. It is assumed that there is present at such interfaces a disso-

[9] Cf. *Interfacial Forces and Phenomena in Physiology,* by Sir W. M. Bayliss, London, 1923.

ciated double layer, the Helmholtz electric double layer. The electrical properties of surfaces in contact (interfaces) exercise important influences on the rate of passage of ions through membranes.

The chemist's knowledge of the structure of surfaces separating immiscible liquids is due largely to Irving Langmuir, though the work of W. G. Hardy and N. K. Adams [10] has considerably extended this knowledge. It is known that when a small amount of a fatty acid (oleic and palmitic acid, lecithin, etc.) is placed on the surface of water it spreads out into a thin film. In order to explain the behavior of such oil-films on water it is assumed that the molecules of the fatty acids are oriented. That is, at the surface of contact there is now a definite arrangement of the molecules. In the monomolecular layers which are thus formed the molecules are perpendicular to the surface and parallel to each other, with the carboxyl group attached to the water and the long paraffin chains pointing away from the water. When molecules are oriented in films in this way the physical properties of both are altered.

The theoretical aspect of the subject was advanced a step further when Hardy showed that a molecule surrounded by an unsymmetrical field of force, if situated at an interfacial region where one fluid meets another, will have a minimum potential energy when oriented in one particular direction. Thermal agitations tend to break up orientation. The substance of Hardy's theory is that orientation will occur when the tendency to come to a position of minimal potential energy is strong enough

[10] Cf. "The Properties and Molecular Structure of Thin Films," by N. K. Adams, *Proceedings of the Royal Society of London*, Series A, 1922, Vol. 101, 452-472.

Some of the biological applications of these ideas are discussed in the treatise, *Lecithin and Allied Substances*, by Hugh Maclean and Ida S. Maclean, 1927.

to *prevent* the molecules from rotating freely in the course of Brownian movements. Here again we see microscopic random forces yielding their freedom of motion to higher types of dominance.

Perhaps at this point the reader would like to ask, What has all this to do with "emergence"? The answer is that when we know the story better it will appear that these matters have much to do with organic emergence. Already the rôle of orientation of molecules in biochemical processes is being studied. According to some theorists the migrations of ions through semi-permeable membranes—such as occur, for example, in nerve conduction —could not take place were it not for the fact that the molecules of membranes have an electrical moment, and under the influence of fields of force are capable of rotating in such a way that the longest axis of the molecule takes a position perpendicular to the membrane, thus allowing moving ions to slip through. Here again the orientation of molecules underlying nervous transmission and integration is subordinate to some dominating plan, which, as in the case of the bubble, is a nonsummative whole ordering the parts.

All this seems very abstruse. And yet it is just such complexly interdependent processes which form the biochemical substratum of organic behavior and conscious unity. Out of this variety and intricacy that new simplicity emerges which is grasped introspectively in the unity of our psychic life. How can we picture such a synthesis and alchemy?

Let us suppose that our mind's eye is an X-ray instrument capable of ultra-microscopic vision. What sort of picture would we see when we thus look into the brain of a person whose cerebral processes were revealed to us? In the first place, we would probably verify the postulate of Troland [11] that a visual sensation can scarcely be attributed to the function of any cerebral component smaller than a single synapse. We should probably also verify Troland's surmise that a single synaptic mechanism involves the simultaneous coöperation of millions of physical atoms, electrons and electric and magnetic fields. It would probably also be discovered that when we consciously perceive (experience) the color "red," the excitation of the cortical receiver (neurone) which is responsible for the production of that conscious quality is a function of the discharge frequency of that cell. But the most detailed analysis might very well show that the number of ions which are involved in the synaptic activity is not always the same numerically. That is, two experiences of "redness" will be perceived to be the "same" when they approximate closely the *average* number of ionic permeations necessary to make the response frequency of that cell conform to the "all or none" law of nervous excitation. In other words, with finer means of measurement the *all or none law* would probably be shown to be an expression of the fact that a specific cell's response represents a rather stable statistical constancy of response.

When one reviews the facts about nerve conduction and sensory perception, with the end in view of formulating a theory of the neuro-conscious process, it becomes obvious that the only hypothesis which fits the facts of the *specificity* and *variability* of nerve function is L. Lapicque's doctrine of *chronaxy*.[12] Keeping in mind, then, that the concept of chronism probably provides the best

[11] "The Physical Basis of Nerve Functions," by L. T. Troland, *Psychological Review*, 1920, Vol. 27, 323-350.
[12] For a brief survey of the facts of sensory perception in relation to the doctrine of chronaxy see the writer's booklet, *The Alchemy of Light and Color*.

substitute for the older "specific energies" theory of the nervous system, let us return to our problem of trying to envisage the processes which take place in the cortex when a conscious process is initiated.

According to the theory of neuronic attunement here favored, nerve conduction is a process dependent upon the passage of nerve impulses across the synaptic junctions of neurones which are in "tune" (or "isochronous") with each other. By way of forming a conceptual picture of the microscopic physical details of this process recall the following points: (1) we know that every living cell is limited by a semi-permeable membrane; (2) according to Overton this membrane may possess a lipoid, or fatty acid, film in which the molecules are oriented; (3) from the work of Langmuir and others we know that when a very small amount of fatty acid is placed on the surface of the water it forms a film which may be only a molecule in thickness; (4) we know that these molecules are not arranged indiscriminately, but are perpendicular to the surface and parallel to each other; (5) we also know, from the work of W. D. Harkins, that these molecules, which are longer than they are wide, are like compass needles, in that they can rotate on an axis under the influence of electric and magnetic fields of force; (6) and that these lipoid films—of lecithin, for example —which are present in the brain might make nerve conduction possible by permitting the passage of charged particles (ions) when the orientation of the molecules capable of rotation is reversed by an alteration of the electromotive force.

It is known that in the process of nerve conduction two correlative phenomena are involved: there is a wave of *polarization* accompanied by an increase of *permeability* to the ions which are progressing along the conductance path. When one tries to explain this dual process it is necessary to determine how much is due to the structure of the cell membrane and how much to the film of adsorbed molecules attached to the membrane (cell wall). In the interesting view presented by H. M. Johnson [13] the mechanism of chronism ("tuning") is visualized in terms of neurones with permanent membranes acting as sieves. Thus Bayliss' notion of a "limiting" membrane is rejected as inadequate to perform the functions which chronism requires. According to Johnson, the *surface-membrane* has a *surface-film*, which is simply the Helmholtz electric double layer present at all interfaces, such as are found at the synapses formed by neuronic junctures. The surface-membrane is selectively permeable to this layer of ionized molecules *adsorbed* to the surface membrane. When the field of force is constant the elements of the membrane assume a definite orientation, and a reversal of orientation, produced by an alteration of the electromotive force, is necessary to render the film permeable to an ion to which it was previously impermeable. Dr. Johnson assumes that the time required for the reversal of orientation of the molecules of the surface-film is specific for a given cell, and that the reciprocal of the orientation-time represents the number of oscillations of the surface charge. This film-frequency, F, bears a mathematical relation to the discharge frequency, f, of the cell. Thus the film of the cell is conceived to be analogous to the grid of a thermionic tube, acting as a tuner.

In this beautifully simple scheme all the problems of learning, thinking, attention, inhibition, transfer of function, etc., reduce to a simple mathematical problem

[13] See his article in the *Journal of Comparative Psychology*, 1927, Vol. 7, 187-235.

of finding the highest common factor in the discharging-frequency of the afferent cells and the charging frequency of the efferent ones! "Learning" becomes nothing but the forcing of oscillation-periods of neurones into efficient relation with each other. And the "all or none" law finds its explanation (in part) in the orientation-time of molecules.

It is undoubtedly true that this picture of the nature of the nervous functions is inadequate and needs to be modified, but it has the great merit of trying to give a concrete picture of what may be happening in the cortex when a conscious experience is in process. The present writer has indicated the directions in which this modification ought to move; one line of development we have proposed is that we try to secure a better understanding of the nature and *modus operandi* of the field forces which are active in the conduction processes. This leads us into that obscure region of catalysis, a province wherein fools may rush, though angels fear to tread.

V. Consciousness and Electricity

We are now at the stage where it is necessary to investigate whether, and if so in what way, radiation may play a rôle in the symphonic organization which emerges as consciousness. If light is to play a rôle it must enter in the guise of a prompter to the other actors taking part in the cerebral drama which goes on inside our skulls. Let us see how this is possible.

Chemical reactions in which light plays a rôle are called photochemical reactions. Everyone who has been sunburned, or used a photographic camera, is familiar with the fact that light has the power to bring about photochemical reactions. The following classification of photochemical reactions is not exhaustive; but for our purposes these kinds of reactions are of most interest:

1. *Irreversible Photochemical Reactions.*—In this class we find photo-catalytic reactions, in which light facilitates a unidirectional process. Thus formaldehyde may be synthesized from carbon dioxide, in the presence of a catalyst such as colloidal uranium, by exposure to light.

2. *Reversible Photochemical Reactions.*—Here there is an equilibrium condition which can swing in either direction, accordingly as the substance is in the dark or in the light. The decomposition of silver chloride under the influence of light into silver and chlorine and their recombination in the dark is an illustration of this type of reversible reaction. Selig Hecht has proposed the idea that when light strikes the light-sensitive elements of the eye a reversible reaction takes place which is made possible by the visual purple of the retina.

Several laws of photochemistry have been formulated. These are as follows:

1. *Grotthus's Law.*—This law states that radiation must be absorbed in order to bring about the reaction which it produces.

2. *Roscoe-Bunson Law.*—This law states that the amount of substance decomposed by radiant energy is proportional to the amount of radiant energy absorbed. In other words, the amount of substance decomposed is proportional to the product of the intensity of light by the time during which it acts. The behavior of heliotropic animals conforms to this law.

It is an interesting fact that radiations of different wave-length may produce different reactions in the same substance. For example, it appears to be a fairly general rule that of two radiations which produce opposite effects, *it is the longer wave-length which produces the oxidizing action and the shorter wave-length which produces the reducing action.* This fact suggests the interesting question of whether light may not make possible the oxidation-reduction processes in the brain, and, if so, whether this may not be of importance in explaining the physiological conditions of consciousness.

On another occasion the writer has tried to show that a possible biochemical basis for the differences in electrical potential in different parts of the cortex may lie in the oxidation-reduction rhythms (redox-potentials) well known in inorganic and organic processes. The temptation is strong to believe that the relativity of cerebral action currents which experiments reveal are a manifestation of the bioelectric relativity of redox-potentials. This idea of oxidation-reduction rhythms fits in nicely with the view that every organic substance in the body has *in relation to every other* a certain redox-potential, which varies according to such conditions as hydrogen ion concentration, temperature, oxygen concentration, the catalytic agents present, etc. Given this, we can then go on to point out that light frequently acts as a catalyst in chemical reactions and that this is especially true of processes involving oxidation and reduction. Next bring in the fact that of two radiations which produce opposite effects, it is the longer wave-lengths which produce the oxidizing action and the shorter wave-lengths which produce the reducing reaction and we have all the elements necessary for a truly relativistic biochemistry! All we need to do now is add a new assumption: "short" and "long" wave-lengths are relative; for example, as compared with ultra-violet light, yellow rays are long, but as compared with infra-red rays they are short. If redox-potentials are due to relative differences, to bring about oxidation-reduction rhythms subjectively a *relative* difference in wave-length is required.

In the brain neural integration would then be interpreted in this fashion. The sensory cortex reacts (experiences) in terms of its previous "set," and to bring about a response the motor cortex sends forth the particular frequency which integrates the sensory components with the motor rhythms. This makes the brain a kind of *master-clock*—a "pace-maker" which adjusts the "local" times of neurone-frequencies to each other.

A possible difficulty with the foregoing theory of biochemical relativity arises out of some comments on the foregoing view presented by Dr. Hudson Hoagland. Professor Hoagland's view is that redox-potentials are not primarily responsible for bioelectric potentials. Pseudoequilibria, maintained by dynamic steady states in which diffusion potentials play a predominant rôle, seem to offer a better basis for bioelectric effects, according to Professor Hoagland. These effects are, in general, maintained by irreversible chemical reactions. This might seem to eliminate, or diminish the importance of, reversible reactions, in cerebral processes, though it still leaves us the other alternative—irreversible photochemical reactions to play with.

VI. The Radiation Hypothesis in Chemistry

It is one thing to formulate laws of photochemistry and quite another thing to explain these laws—or any laws of chemistry. At the present time the mechanism of even the simplest chemical reaction is not understood. To be sure, there are theories about the observed facts. The beginning of modern theories of chemical reactivity dates with the year 1889, when the Swedish chemist, Svanté Arrhenius, supposed that the chemical constituents of a reaction are not reactive in their ordinary states, but must first be "activated" before they can take part in a chemical reaction. This fertile assumption was the first step in a line of speculation which produced the conception known as the *radiation theory of chemical activation*. Such a view is explicitly accepted by Perrin when he assumes that every chemical reaction is accompanied either by the absorption or emission of light.

The notion of "activated states" was proposed before the modern developments in the quantum theory of energy. Since the work of Max Planck, who first proposed the revolutionary view that energy comes in parcels or in bundles, activated states have been identified with the higher quantum states of the molecules or atoms. It is not necessary to elaborate the details of this theory; suffice it to say that in 1905 Einstein extended Planck's quantum theory by introducing the notion of *light quanta*. And a further advance was made in 1912 when Einstein formulated his law of photochemistry, which states that the number of chemically reacting molecules is equal to the number of absorbed light quanta.

The radiation hypothesis is especially attractive in dealing with processes where the relation between chemical reactions and radiation is reversible. The postulate of reversibility appeals to the chemist because it seems to apply to certain phenomena of photoluminescence, namely, *phosphorescence* and *fluorescence*. These terms designate, respectively, whether the period of glow of the luminescent substance is long or short. The phenomena of fluorescence and phosphorescence are the reverse of photochemical processes. That is, as we have seen, in a photochemical process light quanta are absorbed and excite the molecules, and in this state, presumably because of their increased energy, they are able to take part in chemical reactions not otherwise possible. But when atoms and molecules radiate light it is supposed that their previously absorbed light quanta are again radiated out into space.

The problem of determining and explaining the facts of photoluminescence takes the investigator into the field of spectroscopy. According to the now inadequate Bohr theory of the atom the radiation of light is due to a return to a more stable position in the atoms of the electrons which were previously displaced by the exciting radiation. But as is generally known, the Bohr picture has been replaced by the de Broglie-Schrödinger wave picture, and so the ideas about "excited" atoms need to be revised. This has actually been done for simple atoms, but molecular phenomena and chemical reactions are more complex, and, except in a few cases, wave mechanics has not yet been applied in the field of chemistry. When it is, it will of necessity be compelled to accept whatever facts have already been established, and to that extent it will merely give us a new interpretation of the old facts.

And now again we ask, What has this to do with the phenomena of life? And the reply is the same as that previously given: when we see the picture more clearly it will be found that "excited" states have much to do with biochemical reactivity. Continued experiment is establishing beyond doubt that *light of one sort or another is always involved in biological processes*. The validity of this statement is independent of the truth or falsity of Nodon's claim that organic substances of high vitality can take their own photographs; it does not compel us to accept Gurwitch's claims for the existence of mitogenetic (M) rays; it does not prove the truth of Dr. Ladd-Franklin's supposition that nerve fibers, when active, give off visible light. Of course, the verification of any, or all, of these claims would constitute a further step in the direction in which we are looking:— the view that the notion of higher quantum states takes some of the mystery out of life processes—organic catalysis, for example—and that life itself is somehow associated with the "excited" states of atoms and molecules of colloidal systems.

It is true that the radiation theory of chemical activation faces several difficulties. For this reason, since the time of Arrhenius, other mechanisms have been proposed to bring about this activation. One theory postulates the collision between two ordinarily unactivated elements with each other. Another view, a compromise between a pure radiation theory and the collision theory, ascribes the activation to a collision between two molecules and a quantum of energy. And so on. But the difficulties which the radiation theory faces are not insuperable. Thus one of the main obstacles encountered by the radiation theory of chemical activation is that of finding a mechanism that will act rapidly enough to keep up with the known rates of reaction. But in commenting on this difficulty, Professor Tolman [14] calls attention to the fact that in the famous Stern and Gerlach experiment on the orientation of atoms in a magnetic field, the atoms orient themselves in an exceedingly short time (10^{-4} sec.) and thus receive energy at a rate far greater than we can account for on the basis of any known mechanism of energy transfer. The only biological parallel to this which the writer is familiar with was brought forward

[14] *Statistical Mechanics*, by Richard C. Tolman, 1927, p. 284.

by J. H. Quastel [15] in 1926, who proposed the interesting theory that the electric charge in the cell surface is concerned in the activation of the molecules of the cell. Thus a molecule is activated and becomes susceptible of oxidation or reduction when it comes under the influence of electric fields. In this view there is a relation between the orientation of molecules in the surface of the cell, the electric fields, and the activation of the molecules.

To the thesis that radiation plays a rôle in organic alchemy the work on bioluminescence contributes valuable factual material. As yet, to be sure, the available facts are not sufficient to prove conclusively that light and life have some fundamental kinship, though, if the present view is correct, this will come in time. The work of Newton Harvey [16] on the oxidation of luciferin, which supplies the energy necessary to activate the molecules in the organisms exhibiting bioluminescence, will probably find its explanation in the more general phenomena of chemiluminescence. In such cases the adsorption which causes the "close packing" of molecules (of the Helmholtz layer previously discussed) is important. This fact has been emphasized by H. Freundlich.[17]

The most general synthesis of the various phenomena we have considered would be attained if photoluminescent and photosynthetic processes could be coupled together in some partnership. The world's basic life process is wrapped up in the secret of how the green leaf converts waste carbon dioxide from the air, and water from the soil, through the use of the sun's energy, into food. It is now suggested by E. C. C. Baly of Liverpool University that the explanation of this photosynthetic process

[15] *Biochemical Journal*, 1926, Vol. 20, p. 166.
[16] Cf. *The Nature of Animal Light*.
[17] Cf. *New Conceptions in Colloidal Chemistry*, London, 1926, p. 12.

may be found in photoluminescent processes, whereby chemicals shine in the dark after exposure to radiation of the proper frequency. Professor Baly is well known for his experiments in which sugar is made out of carbon dioxide and water, through the use of light of short wave length. Now he proposes a radiation theory of chemical activation in which highly activated molecules of matter, as they undergo chemical reactions in photosynthesis, emit critical quanta of radiant energy as visible light in photoluminescence, and thus the chemistry of light is firmly wedded to the physics of light.[18]

VII. THE CARBON CHEMISTRY OF CONSCIOUSNESS

It is generally known that the chemistry of life is the chemistry of carbon compounds. The reasons why carbon forms the building material of organic matter are several. For one thing, because carbon has a high valence and therefore possesses the power of combining with other elements, it can form the basis for the numerous and complex compounds which are the physical basis of life. One of the best examples of this is found in the *fatty acids* previously referred to. This is significant because the fatty acids are the ancestors of the *amino acids,* and the amino acids, in turn, are the constituents which enter into the making of the *proteins.* That is to say, an amino acid is a fatty acid in which nitrogen is incorporated, and proteins, as enormously complicated arrangements of amino acids, are thus nitrogenous colloids.

We have said that proteins differ because of the vary-

[18] In his article on "Phosphorescence, Fluorescence, and Chemical Reaction," in *Nature,* 1928, Vol. 122, 651-654, Baly argues that the radiation theory of chemical activation is not dead and buried, as some authorities have declared. Baly suggests a possible mechanism for activation by infra-red radiation.

ing proportions and arrangements of the amino acids they contain. The best known proteins consist of chains of from 100 to 200 amino acids. It is possible experimentally to combine amino acids until a complex of as many as 18 units is obtained, and the more amino acids are linked together the more the whole resembles the simpler proteins. In Emil Fisher's synthesis the amino acids were linked together by condensing the carboxyl group of each acid. The idea has been put forth that in the proteins the main valence chains are coiled up like a spiral, and this has been taken as the basis for the elasticity exhibited in muscle contraction.[19]

At this point, in connection with the suggestion of a possible spiral structure in protoplasm, it is necessary to digress for a moment, in order to bring out additional reasons why carbon constitutes the building material of life.

It will be recalled from our first section that evolution is regarded as a device for producing organisms capable of dissipating a maximum of cosmic energy through the development of structures which respond to the widest possible environment which the organism can meaningfully simplify. This evolutionary strategy has a precursor, however, in the inorganic world, at least according to the statement of E. E. Fournier D'Albe [20] to the effect that "the atoms always endeavor to take up positions which will give the most scope for vibration. This is another instance of the law of maximum degradation of energy, since the electrons associated with atoms are thus enabled to waste the largest amount of energy in the form of radiant heat." This same principle, D'Albe

[19] Cf. *Physical Chemistry of Living Tissues and Life Processes*, by R. Beutner, 1933, p. 133.
[20] *Contemporary Chemistry*, 1911, p. 52.

believes, is illustrated in inorganic chemistry, and the carbon atom, known to be tetrahedral in shape, is supposed to exemplify this. Thus D'Albe argues (*ibid.*, p. 76) that "if the surface of an atom were elastic, and its volume restricted, and the positive charge within it could expend most energy by spreading over the largest possible surface, the atom would inevitably assume the shape of a tetrahedron."

Whatever the truth in these speculations may be, the fact remains that *it is the symmetrical tetrahedral shape of the carbon atom which endows it with its valence, and it is this which enables it to build up the numerous complicated asymmetrical compounds of living matter*. It is known that the long chain carbon compounds thus produced, which possibly have a spiral or coiled structure, are optically active, or possess the power of rotating a beam of light. According to a current theory, this optical activity is due to the twist given the beam of light by right- and left-handed isomeres of carbon. Whatever the explanations, the reality of optical anisotropy in organic colloids is established and the fact that organic chemistry is the chemistry of asymmetric carbon compounds is beyond dispute.

One of the arguments advanced in favor of a vitalistic theory of life is based on the fact that chemical compounds artificially synthesized have no optical activity, whereas living substances (*e.g.*, malic acid, glucose, etc.) when actually found in organisms turn the plane of polarized light in one direction or another. From this fact Japp and Pasteur concluded that the production of asymmetric compounds is a unique prerogative of life, not to be duplicated in the laboratory. But in commenting on this view it may be pointed out that some experiments show that *polarized* light may influence biological processes in a way quite different from ordinary light. There is a case on record where an optically active substance was formed by purely a physical agent—polarized light.[21] And as D'Arcy W. Thompson [22] points out, portions of the light which come from the sun are already plane-polarized light, and become, in fact, circularly polarized light by reflection at the sea, and also rotated under the influence of terrestrial magnetism. This makes it easier to imagine how light may have built up optically active compounds in the sea, and thus started the stream of life upon its evolutionary career.

The idea that polarized light from the sky, assisted perhaps by the magnetic field of the earth, may have functioned in the original synthesis of life is entirely consistent with, though not dependent upon, the hypothesis of the spiral structure of the protein molecule. Indeed, *the coiled structure may even have been caused by the twist given the chain structures by circularly polarized light*. We know already that ultra-violet light, acting on carbon dioxide and water, produces formaldehyde; and the fact is also established that formaldehyde, under the influence of suitable radiation, may be linked with potassium nitrite to form hydroxamic compounds, and hydroxamic acid may react with activated formaldehyde to produce complex nitrogen-containing compounds resembling the amino acids. Isn't this all of a piece? And doesn't it lend support to the hypothesis of a fundamental kinship between light and life?

If we concentrate on the more detailed study of organic development, the problem then becomes that of explaining how the life process of individual growth

[21] Cf. *New Conceptions in Colloid Chemistry*, by H. Freundlich, 1926, p. 138.
[22] *Growth and Form*, 1917, pp. 416 ff.

which, like the movement of evolution that this growth recapitulates, is correlated with the building up of more complex structures, while the process of death is correlated with the breaking down of higher molecular compounds. One fundamental experimental result that needs to be kept in mind is that just as "normal" tissue is electrically positive to degenerated or dead tissue, so the lower fatty acids are negative to higher ones.[23] This fact provides us with the starting point for a theory which we need: a conception of fatty acids which allows us to regard the building up of complex molecules, and the orientation of molecules at surfaces, as processes controlled by electrical charges.

The notion of protein systems as *condensers* which accumulate electrical charges is not entirely new. The idea that protein molecules can be organized in monomolecular layers which then function as condensers which can transform chemical energy into electrical energy has been proposed by Blinks,[24] though we have already referred to somewhat similar conceptions. It is interesting to note that in this idea Prof. Osterhaut (*ibid.*, p. 220) sees a possible explanation of the remarkable facts concerning the life and death of cells as phenomena dependent upon the permeability of membranes.

Returning now to the development of our own thesis, we note that the organism can be looked at from two points of view: (*a*) at any given moment we may be interested in the *modus operandi* of its behavior as a mature organism, or (*b*) we may be interested in how the thing evolved into that going concern. From our point of view these two interests are not exclusive of

[23] See Beutner, *op. cit.*, p. 243.
[24] Cf. *Molecular Physics in Relation to Biology*, Bulletin of the National Research Council, No. 69, p. 16.

each other. Ontogenetic development is the physiological process whereby the body fabricates for itself a mind. The body, by virtue of its hereditary endowment, is predisposed to build up a chemical structure capable of reacting to certain stimuli. The reception, from earliest infancy, of electrochemical stimuli assists in the organization of the available carbon compounds. Thus in the brain there are elaborated and organized complex cerebral substances (cephalin, cholesterol, lecithin, etc.) and oriented arrangements of molecules at the membrane surfaces. In this process there may be, as D'Arcy W. Thompson says, a comprehensive field of force running through the organism shaping it, independently of the individual cells which enter like froth into its fabric. But, even so, the reception of electrical stimuli from sensory channels becomes a morphogenetic force guiding the development of the plastic materials.

Once a fairly stable structure is built up, with a somewhat specialized localization of functions, we have a biochemical system wherein each synapse, thus evolved, acts as a condenser system transmuting chemical energy into electrical energy—bioelectric potentials. The minute toll taken from each interface builds up a mental field, and this, in turn, becomes capable of controlling the entire cortex, with its complex synaptic system, through a dominance of pattern due to a hierarchy of organization, metabolism and electrical potential. And thus the action of consciousness on the body appears as the inverse of the process of the production of mind from matter. For the mental field activates the molecules, and the neurone undergoes an oxidation-reduction rhythm, responding according to the "all or none" law by using up its own supply of potential energy. Cerebral integration, facilitation and inhibition are aspects of the inter-neuronic adjustments of rhythms of discharge (chronaxies) of cortical frequencies. This view not only helps explain the facts indicating that intelligence and feeble-mindedness are related to the ratio of lecithin to cholesterol in the brain, but, coupled with the idea of Dr. Crile [25] that potassium (the only radioactive element in the body) has the power to organize and orient a system, it provides us with a basis for understanding how radiations internally produced may in turn act on the body, with its synaptic system, and raise it to higher energy levels of behavior.

And so, generalizing this development of knowledge, we conclude that we seem to be a little closer to that distant goal of an understanding of how superior mental patterns superimpose their fields of force upon the quantum-colloidal configurations and activate their subordinate molecular fields, thereby guiding and modifying the bodily mechanisms of behavior. The macroscopic field of consciousness emerges out of its microscopic constituents, but in turn it lives to dominate its subordinate rhythms through the electromagnetic bond of fealty which unites body and mind.

[25] *A Bipolar Theory of Living Processes,* by George W. Crile, 1926, pages 132 and 208.

CHAPTER VIII

CONSCIOUSNESS AS A NEW DIMENSION

I. Time and Mind

In the preceding chapters we have tried to state a form of naturalism free from the limitations of historical materialism and mechanism. This is done on the basis of the thesis that modern physics makes untenable the older mechanistic materialism, without altering the status or tenets of naturalism.

In trying to develop the possible implications of the new physics for philosophy and psychology the writer has on several occasions [1] pointed out that the new wave mechanics promises to provide a place in physical reality for many of the properties of psychic life, and that eventually dualistic and vitalistic theories will be unnecessary in order to explain biological and psychological phenomena.[2] In developing such a doctrine the problem of the theory of color vision must of necessity be considered. The idea presented is substantially the view as stated in Chapter IV of the present book, viz., that in color vision a process is reinstated in the cortical receivers of the visual area analogous to the external frequencies of light which are the external "cause" of the color experience.

[1] Cf. "Light, Wave Mechanics, and Consciousness," *Journal of Philosophy,* 1928, Vol. 25, 309-317; "Contributions of the New Physics to Philosophy and Psychology," *Psyche,* 1930, Vol. 11, 65-87.
[2] The same view is taken by J. B. S. Haldane in his paper on "Quantum Mechanics as a Basis for Philosophy," *Philosophy of Science,* 1934, Vol. I, 78-98.

The end-result of biological evolution has been to produce a structure, the brain-eye, which can act as a kind of step-up transformer, generating in consciousness the *similarity of logical structure* which the mathematicians call "isomorphism." That is to say, in addition to the assumption that *the nerve process preserves something analogous to all the properties of the external wave frequencies and foreshadows all the characteristics of the cortical process, the additional assumption is made that in the brain there is reinstated a typical form of undulatory phenomenon somehow corresponding to the original wave frequencies which acted as the stimulus.*[3]

If we generalize Schrödinger's doctrine of wave mechanics, we can interpret the matter (corpuscular) aspect of all physical configurations as repeating sets of wave patterns of electrical density, which have associated with them field forces that do not repeat themselves in that "same" region of space, but radiate out into space.[4] Neurones, no less than atoms, are then conceived to be undulation-patterns of such a sort that we can superimpose upon the *chronaxies* (or neurone-frequencies of discharge) second order undulations of an electromagnetic nature, so that consciousness becomes a unity of force-fields and the soul becomes the harmony of the body.

In elaborating this doctrine the suggestion arises that since there are waves and waves, perhaps harmonic analysis will have to add to the present categories of waves (longitudinal, transverse, etc.) other types of wave motions, even involving additional dimensions, before we

---

[3] Quoted from *The Alchemy of Light and Color,* p. 61.

[4] It is true that in the "sub-ether" of wave mechanics the velocity of radiation (in a super-dispersive medium) becomes variable, and energy travels at velocities which become slower as the wave-length is increased. On this matter see G. P. Thomson's *The Atom* (Home University Library), pp. 185-186, and H. T. Flint's *Wave Mechanics,* p. 35.

can find the kind of symphonic organization which represents consciousness. The notion that consciousness is a new dimension which, like time, intersects the physical universe at right angles to a "lower" spatial view finds some support in the theory of relativity. Many expounders of Einstein's theory have pointed out that it is consciousness which stratifies the four-dimensional space-time manifold of relativity into a three-dimensional static order and a one-dimensional irreversible order of change. Apparently it was this fact which suggested to T. B. Robertson,[5] A. P. Mathews,[6] and W. P. Montague[7] the connection between consciousness, time and a higher dimension.

The interest of the writer in these matters was in part due to a study of S. Alexander's work, *Space, Time and Deity*. Professor Alexander's formula is this: *time is the mind of space*. Alexander compares his own theory of the relation of time to space with that of the doctrine of relativity, but of course he was unable at that time to take into account the doctrine of wave mechanics. In the version presented by the present writer an effort is made to find confirmation for the concept of consciousness as an undulation pattern in the higher dimensions which the new quantum theory—wave mechanics —postulates. Here we may appeal to some of the views stated by Sir J. J. Thomson and Sir J. H. Jeans. As Professor Thomson[8] points out, a moving electron is a much more complicated thing than a small point charge of electricity in motion. A moving electron is always ac-

[5] "Consciousness and the Sense of Time," *Scientific Monthly*, June, 1923.
[6] "The Reduction of all Physical Dimensions to those of Space and Time," *Journal of the Washington Academy of Science*, 1923, 195-210.
[7] "Time and the Fourth Dimension," *University of California Publications in Philosophy*, 1925, 183-207.
[8] *Beyond the Electron*, 1928, Cambridge University Press.

companied by a series of waves, and these waves have complete control over its path; the electron is compelled to follow the lead of the waves. In other words, *the electron provides its own ether in the form of waves, and these waves show the electron where to go.*

In the most general form this conclusion tells us that every material aggregate carries with it its own ether— just as every man carries with him his own rainbow—in the sense that its behaviors and motion are controlled by the potentials of interacting systems of particles. On the level of conscious organisms this permits us to regard the transition from the objective (brain) to the subjective (consciousness) as analogous to the relation between the corpuscular feature of the electrons and the undulatory feature of the waves which direct their motions. But here the ordinary three-dimensional framework of Newtonian physics, or even the four-dimensional space-time continuum of relativity theory, is inadequate to picture the events of such complex physical interactions.

This view that there is no way of representing in the three-dimensional space of materialism the properties of psychic life is in harmony with the suggestion of Professor Jeans [9] that consciousness may lie outside the four-dimensional continuum of relativity theory, and that we should not make the mistake of trying to force happenings which occur in many dimensions into a smaller number of dimensions. Of course the objection which will be urged against this view is that there is no evidence for the physical existence of this many-dimensional configuration-space. This is true, if "physical" evidence means sensory evidence, for we have already asserted that the evolution of vision has conspired to exclude from sensory perception field-forces. But we have

[9] *The Mysterious Universe,* 1930, p. 133.

also affirmed that the unperceived underpinning of the "material" world is no less real than the surface phenomena which affect our senses. Another reply to this difficulty has also been given when Jeans argues (*op. cit.*, pp. 129-130), in opposition to the view that the multi-dimensional space required by wave mechanics for the more complicated physical events is but a clever mathematical dodge, that a seven-dimensional space of two electrons does not possess a lower degree of reality than the waves of a single electron, which are real enough to record themselves on a photographic plate.

In order to clarify the conception of mind as a new dimension, bearing a relation of similarity of logical structure to the corresponding brain processes, it is necessary to present the logical fundamentals of the theory of isomorphism.

II. Logical Structure and Dimensionality

The development of the notion of logical structure is due largely to Bertrand Russell.[10] The fundamental ideas have been further generalized by C. J. Keyser in his theory of *doctrinal functions* and H. M. Sheffer in his theory of *system functions*. While these ideas have thus far not entered into the fabric of science, a beginning in this direction is being made and one may look for rapid progress in this field in the near future. In one field isomorphism is well recognized: in mathematics in the subject of *group theory*. The importance of this approach for science has recently been shown by Hermann Weyl.[11] In the form of topology (dealing with such concepts as

[10] See his *Introduction to Mathematical Philosophy*, Chapters IV and VI, and *Principia Mathematica* (Whitehead and Russell), Vol. ii, Part iv.
[11] *The Theory of Groups and Quantum Mechanics*, Eng. trans., 1932.

continuity, ordered sets, dimensionality, etc.) the theory of isomorphism shows us how to deal with the ordering of physical events in space-time, as L. L. Whyte [12] has indicated.

As is readily understood, the most fundamental idea presupposed by *isomorphism* is the notion of *order*. For our purposes the most important type of order is the physical order of space-time, but this leads us directly into the subject of isomorphism, since our notion of physical order presupposes a similarity of relation-structure between geometrical (conceptual) space and physical space. It is an interesting fact that the fundamental and universal order of space and time is the order illustrated by the series of natural integers. For this reason the term *serial order* is very convenient. Serial order is based on what mathematical logic terms *irreflexive, transitive* and *asymmetrical* relations, and covers such relations as succession in time, positions in space, and quantitative magnitudes. The principles which express the facts about serial order are like the postulates of any *deductive system,* and may therefore be put in the following typical form:

(A) BASE: a class, K, of entities, x, y, z, etc., and a relation or rule of operation, R.

(B) POSTULATES:

    (1) xRx is false throughout the class K. This is the property of irreflexiveness: no element x has R to itself.

    (2) For any two elements, x and y, of K, either xRy or yRx. This states the property of asymmetry.

    (3) For any three elements, x, y and z, of K, if xRy and yRz, then xRz. This states the property of transitivity.

[12] *Critique of Physics,* 1932, pp. 153 ff.

If we let $f(x)$ mean that x belongs to the class, and specify that our relation, R, means specifically "is larger than" $(L=R)$, and represent it thus: $L\ (x,\ y)$, then we may restate our postulates as follows:

(1) $(x) \cdot f\ (x) \supset \sim L\ (x, x)$.
(2) $(x, y) : f\ (x) \cdot f\ (y) \cdot \sim (x = y) \cdot \supset L\ (x, y)\ v\ L\ (y, x)$.
(3) $(x, y, z) : f\ (x) \cdot f\ (y) \cdot f\ (z) \cdot L\ (x, y) \cdot L\ (y, z) \cdot \supset \cdot x\ L\ z$.

The symbolic formulæ read like the first set of postulates, except for the substitution of L for R.

While the notion of serial order is employed in the concept of isomorphism, the latter notion is especially applicable when we are comparing two domains, both of which have a "base" and a set of postulates which obey the logical structure of serial order. Thus if two deductive systems have the same "structure" they are isomorphic and have common properties. In other words, if every element of one system, S_1, matches an element of another system, S_2, and the generating relation of S_1 is similar to that of S_2, then the two systems have identical logical properties. Instances of such isomorphism are as follows:

(1). A map and the territory which the map represents.
(2). The plot of a novel and the moving picture reproduction.
(3). The score on a musical sheet, the wavy lines on a phonograph record, the music as a series of air vibrations, the corresponding excitations carried by the auditory nerve, and the melody and harmony as experienced in consciousness.
(4). The external physical pattern, the corresponding retinal mosaic, and the phenomenal visual pattern.
(5). The inverse square law as it applies to gravitational and magnetic attraction, and as illustrated by the spreading out into space of sound and light waves.

(6). Any *gestalt*, the elements of which can be *transposed* while yet keeping the same *form,* or logical structure.

These examples illustrate the importance of *isomorphism* for science. The value of such procedure rests upon the fact that when a postulate set is stated in such form that deductions are possible, (a) *the implications of the system may be studied without reference to the question of the material truth or falsity of the set; and* (b) *a number of concrete "interpretations" of that postulate set may be found.* This is the case in each of the above (6) instances of isomorphic structures. It needs to be remembered, however, that two systems possessing a common sub-system may be incompatible with each other at some points.[13]

If the present view is correct, the connection of the foregoing logical machinery with the problem of consciousness is twofold: (A) there must be some similarity of structure between conscious patterns and neural patterns, so that in a developed form psycho-analysis and behaviorism must appear as *interpretations* of a more fundamental biological postulate set; and (B), if we treat time as a one-dimensional component of a space-time manifold, there must be a correspondence (one-one or one-many) between the temporal dimension of consciousness and the spatial coördinates of the physical system.

Since, as already noted, it is consciousness which stratifies a space-time manifold in such a way that the highest dimension is the one-dimensional and irreversible time-axis, the temptation is strong to identify consciousness with the time-coördinate. If, as Minkowski says, three-dimensional dynamics becomes four-dimensional statics,

[13] On this matter see the excellent discussion in *An Introduction to Logic and Scientific Method,* by Morris R. Cohen and Ernest Nagel, 1934, pp. 137-141.

consciousness must be the experience of temporal passage (*duration*) as aroused in us by the sensory reception of stimuli, correlated with the subjective discrimination of physiological rhythms. But, as previously pointed out, while relativity theory requires only a fourfold continuum, quantum mechanics now requires more. In each case the lower dimension of any hyperspace may be regarded as expressing the *static* (or "matter") aspect, with the orthogonal time-axis representing the *dynamic* (or "consciousness") aspect, having associated with it the radiating field forces. From this point of view the most general formula for expressing the relation of consciousness to the body is this:

$$\frac{Consciousness}{Body} = \frac{n+1\text{-}dimensional\ space}{n\text{-}dimensional\ space}$$

In all such cases the properties of any "higher" space are arrived at through reasoning by analogy, and this is a matter of isomorphism. Thus:

$$\frac{One\text{-}dimensional\ space}{Two\text{-}dimensional\ space} = \frac{Two\text{-}dimensional\ space}{Three\text{-}dimensional\ space}$$

$$= \frac{Three\text{-}dimensional\ space}{Four\text{-}dimensional\ space}$$

III. Gestalt Theory and Formal Structure

In tracing out the consequences of this doctrine it is to be noted first of all that while there is supposed to be an isomorphism between consciousness and the brain, the type need not be a one-to-one correlation, and indeed, as we have suggested, is more likely to be a one-many type of correlation. This permits us to conclude that for every neural pattern that rises above the sub-cortical level there is a conscious pattern, but it also allows for the possibility that the "same" phenomenal pattern may have as its physiological basis a different cortical pattern at different times. This view we have proposed on the basis of the results indicating that the same cortical tissue may be both active and passive at the same time, because cerebral action currents are such only by virtue of a difference in potential at a given time. Whether, therefore, such a current will appear depends on where one electrode on the brain is with respect to another. Thus neurone A may be passive with respect to neurone B and active with respect to neurone C, as Professor S. Howard Bartley has pointed out to the writer. This seems to support our view that any "element" gets its character from its *relation* to the other elements of the gestalt, and since such a formal structure can be transposed, the same conscious pattern must be capable of being generated by different structural complexes, provided they have the isomorphic relation-structure.

Another implication of the view of consciousness as a new dimension which, like time, intersects the physical universe at right angles, is this: even if we were given a complete and detailed picture of the brain pattern underlying a conscious thought, we could not, without the empirical rule of transposition of isomorphic structures (from neural to conscious), predict the corresponding conscious process. Phenomena are experienced subjectively in the hyper-dimensional manifold of a configuration-space which cannot be perceived by any external observation of the brain in action, or in the physical space-time of the objective universe. It is a curious feature of this view that while mental pictures become a part of "physical" reality, they are forever beyond perception in that material world.

As a possible reconciliation between the behaviorists, who stress the importance of the motor aspect of response, and those who emphasize the importance of the brain as the physical seat of mental life, we suggest, not that the brain can function independently of the receptor (sensory) and effector (motor) systems, but that it, the brain, adds a qualitative ingredient which is an integration of the sensory and motor components, a synthesis which presents the element of qualitative novelty known as the conscious side of the pattern. Since the entire peripheral apparatus of the body seems to constitute a resonator for the brain, we may, in the language of Aristotle, say that the soul is the *form* of the body. This doctrine could readily be assimilated to present-day gestalt psychology, and, curiously enough, the nexus comes through poetry—as set forth in the following lines from Edmund Spenser's *Hymn in Honor of Beauty:*

> *For the soule the bodie forme doth take,*
> *For soule is forme, and doth the bodie make.*

Another consequence of this view is that it lends support to the idea that man is in some sense an epitome of the universe. A further development of the modernized version of man as a microcosm comes through the quantitative comparison of man's relative position in the middle of the scale of being which ranges from atoms at the lower limit to stars at the upper limit. Metaphorically speaking, the human brain constitutes a kind of nodal point in the vibrating strings of atoms-stars, or perhaps an inflection point in the cosmic curve of action.

Man stands at the cross-roads of the universe, where

intersect the two cones leading, in one direction, towards
the infra-realm of the very small, and, in the opposite
direction, towards the supra-universe of the very large.
In him, in the distinction between brain and consciousness, we find the replica of that pervasive dualism which
is coextensive with the entire domain of nature,—the
dichotomy of particles and waves. Perhaps this parallel
is something more than an analogy. If so, we have an
answer to the question of whether the cosmos has a mind,
i.e., whether it is the expression of the thought of a Great
Mathematician, as Professor Jeans suggests. Then, too,
just as in the individual organism logical patterns play
over the brain as an electric sign over a bank of lights, so
the mathematical patterns of the Cosmic Thinker play
over the surface of physical reality.[14] Professor Lashley has
suggested that the stimulations coming from the brain
represent an *interference pattern* of overlapping fields
of influence. When we recall that in the undulatory
theory of matter of wave mechanics a radiating atom is
pictured as an interference pattern, with "beats" (as in
music) arising out of the superposition of *group waves*,
this idea of the relation of thought (logical patterns) to
physical matter takes on added interest. It is true that in
human thinking the individual does not create the matter of the brain through which thought structures make
their way; but in the case of the Cosmic Mind there
may be a sense in which thought creates (gives logical
form) to matter. This would be so in so far as there is
reason to believe that the group waves are more fundamental than the particle aspect of nature. And perhaps
this is what Jeans [15] means when he tells us that "we may

[14] This is an extrapolation of an analogy from K. S. Lashley's book,
Brain Mechanisms and Intelligence, 1929, Ch. XI.
[15] *The Mysterious Universe*, p. 129.

think of electrons as objects of thought, and time as the process of thinking." If this is not what Jeans means, then what he says is nonsense to me.

IV. Thought and the Brain

The final justification for our thesis involves a restatement of the procedure of creative thinking in the inductive sciences.

Let us begin with what everyone accepts: that thinking begins with the appearance of a problem. A problem arises when we face a situation to which we must respond, but this situation contains elements of novelty for which our ready-made responses are not entirely adequate. In order that we may solve the problem, or explain the situation, we must develop an hypothesis, which then needs to be tested and verified. It is recognized that the most important method of obtaining hypotheses is through *reasoning by analogy*. Analogical reasoning is based on the idea that in so far as the present situation resembles a previous situation, to that extent the solution to the previous problem will be applicable in the present case. Since reasoning by analogy resembles a *proportion* in mathematics, it may be summarized in the following symbolic form:

$$a : b :: c : d \text{ or } \frac{new\ problem}{old\ problem} = \frac{new\ solution}{old\ solution}$$

Elsewhere [16] I have tried to show that the "insight" which gestalt theory regards as so fundamental a constituent of intelligence is nothing more than such reasoning by analogy.

[16] "The Logic of Gestalt Psychology," *Psychological Review*, 1931, Vol. 38, 359-368.

If we seek for the basis of this intellectual procedure in mathematical logic, it will be found in the isomorphic properties of two similar domains. If there is a complete isomorphism the two domains are identical; but no two *physical* situations are ever absolutely identical, since, for one thing, they can never occupy the same space-time. Thus physical identity is really a limiting case of analogy, as two things become more and more alike. In mathematics and symbolic logic we can disregard this physical fact; just as geometrical (conceptual Euclidian) space has properties not met with in actual (physical) space—being homogeneous and isotropic, for example— so pure mathematical logic can ignore the fact of the localization of domains in space-time. Nevertheless, if light and logic bear some fundamental relation to each other, and to the mind, as we have previously argued, we must be able to discover some principle of isomorphism between them.

Let us take seriously the analogy of inductive thinking as a process of enlarging the *sphere of knowledge*. If the field of the known is like an expanding sphere, then at two different times we may have two spheres, one inside the other. Between the two spheres there is a one-to-one correspondence. If we regard the center of the spheres as a point source of light, which radiates out into space, then any "pencil" of radiation which penetrates the first sphere will penetrate the second: there is an isomorphism to the extent that for every point on the one sphere there is a corresponding point on the other. And just as a logical analogy becomes an identity when the "symbolic distance" (to use Scott Buchanan's term) between two similar structures becomes less and less, so the convergence of one sphere upon a smaller results in their coincidence (identity) when their radii become equal. Any point source of light in geometrical space is like a material point (atom) in physical space. In the brain the point source of an analogous process is the minimal volume-element which can be the center of a diffusion process. If our hypothesis is tenable, along with the biochemical diffusion process in the cortex there must be an electromagnetic diffusion process, a wave spreading outward into space.

The speed of thought in the body is limited by the velocity of neural processes; but the speed of thought in free space may be anything that wave mechanics permits or requires. That thoughts are space-time facts is not new; but that mental images, like light, can spread out in the mental dimension of a configuration-space is an implication of physics which most materialists have failed to see. This, however, is not mysterious, for if the thesis of the present volume is correct, we see for the most part only what we are looking for.

If I were to attempt to summarize the burden of the foregoing argument it would amount to this: If it be true that the morphogenetic forces of nature have controlled the evolutionary fabrication of sensori-motor organization, it is no less true that the evolving organism, through its creative elaboration of sensitized detectors, gives a local habitation and a name to hitherto unseen sights and unheard music. Emerson realized something of the import of evolution when he stated that *perception has a destiny.* It may indeed be true, as modern science tells us, that out of starlight we are born; by starlight we live; and into stardust we will all eventually dissolve,— but let us not forget, as Plato finely says, that *light is no ignoble thing!* Perhaps that is what Walter Pater had in mind when he affirmed that "color is a spirit upon things by which they become expressive to the spirit."

In the foregoing pages I have tried, in my own prosaic way, to show how the reality of vision leads us on to visions of reality. It is through the alchemy of light and color that nature progressively reveals herself to herself. In the following chapter, the last of Part I, I shall try to show how this evolutionary movement finally culminates in what is termed the "religion of light."

CHAPTER IX

THE RELIGION OF LIGHT

I. THE UNIVERSALITY OF RELIGION

IT IS common knowledge that there is no subject which is arousing more widespread interest and discussion than the subject of religion. While, on the one hand, religion is being attacked by those who, in an earlier age would have been called "infidels," it is, on the other hand, being extolled by its defenders with equal vigor and eloquence. It appears obvious to the detached onlooker that in this great to-do more heat than light is being generated. In such cases it sometimes turns out that an attempt to get at fundamentals helps to clarify the situation. Such an analysis would attempt, among other things, to answer the question of what the origin of religion may be. In general, a natural history of the genesis and evolution of religion would appear to be a necessary prolegomena to the attempt to answer such questions as to whether religion has been, or need be, a curse upon the human race, as such iconoclasts as Harry Elmer Barnes believe, or whether it is the greatest boon and blessing to humanity, as most religious thinkers hold.

In the present chapter I shall attempt such an analysis as just suggested, and shall try to answer the questions appropriate to such an investigation.

One of the most obvious and significant facts about religion is its universality. It thrives in all places and ap-

pears at all times in human history. We have it on the
authority of Voltaire that if God did not exist it would
be necessary for human beings to create Him. This is
only another way of bringing out the truth of the observation concerning the universality of the religious consciousness.

Religious beliefs and practises have taken many forms
on this planet of ours. Scientific curiosity leads us to wonder how this widespread reaction which we call the religious consciousness has come about. Why is religion seemingly a "psychic necessity"? Is man "incurably religious"
because there is in him an innate consciousness of some
higher reality, the "Supreme Being"? This seems to be
the view of the devotees of religion. Through the ages
men have bowed in reverence to some Cosmic Power
which makes for righteousness, as they understand it,
because they verily believe that there *is* such a Power
over and above nature. This view of the origin of religion
is frequently attached to a supernaturalistic theory of
nature.

The adherents of religion frequently believe that the
concepts of their religion were given to man through
some supernormal process of inspiration or revelation.
According to this view, in all human beings there has
been placed an intuitive consciousness of the existence of
some higher reality than can be grasped through the
senses. The religious impulse is therefore regarded as
something more than a "sublimation" of some biological
craving. The fact of religion, it is argued, compels the
recognition of something in man and the universe which
cannot be explained in terms of the "father complex" of
the psychoanalyst. As Sir Oliver Lodge once said, "It cannot be that the instinct which has led to the erection of
cathedrals and churches in every village is wholly mis-

taken and misleading. There must be some great truth underlying the instinct for worship, and that truth, if it could only be grasped, must be more important to humanity in general than all the conveniences and applications which the progress of scientific knowledge has put into our hands."

It is one of the fatalities of intellectual evolution that no belief is so sacred that it can escape the microscope of analysis. And so we find those who want to look at this picture through the X-ray eyes of science. These scientific surgeons probe around in man's inner being, cutting away with their scalpels the fat of human nature which masks the hidden mechanisms, always trying to get at the underlying nerve of the human response. Some would say that this obsession to analyze the deepest yearnings of the inner being is a kind of intellectual sadism, but it seems to me that this is a supreme illustration of that impulse towards truthfulness and the sheer desire to understand which is the essence of intellectual honesty. Following up this impulse, which is the mainspring of science, we come upon another, and at first sight opposed, explanation of the origin of religion. This explanation, in contrast with the supernatural explanation, we may call the naturalistic explanation.

Natural explanations of the origin of religion hold that religion arises through the operation of agencies and conditions entirely natural in character. According to this view religion comes into existence as a response on the part of organisms living together in the *milieu* of a common physical environment. The religious reaction is a development out of a natural response to a natural stimulus, and not a mystical response to a supernatural stimulus. This is the view which is here presented and defended. Whether such an interpretation will satisfy the disciples of religion remains to be seen.

One type of investigation tending to confirm the naturalistic and humanistic view of the origin of religion is presented in the study of comparative religion. The striking similarities in the culture-patterns of beliefs and rituals, the notable uniformities in the forms of magic, taboo and ceremonials associated with the various religions, may be interpreted by the naturalistic view in several ways. In the first place we may adopt the view that the similarities in theme and practise have resulted because these structures are different versions of the same story; that is, that the legends and motifs common to religious folklore are borrowings from a common historical source. Several examples may be cited to illustrate the point. The parallels between Hebrew and Persian tales, and the similarities between Greek and Hebrew mythologies—such as the stories that evil entered the world through the curiosity of a woman (Pandora and Eve) —might be explained on the supposition that these myths are borrowings from a common historical source. Again, the similarities in symbolism and worship of Roman Catholicism and Brahmanism have suggested that Occidental religion and Oriental religion have influenced each other. Finally, the fact that he could point to legends throughout the world's mythology of a number of crucified saviors of mankind (Chrishna of India, Prometheus, Indra of Thibet, Mithra of Persia, to mention a few) led Kersey Graves to argue in his once well-known book, *The World's Sixteen Crucified Saviors*, that the Christian story of Jesus was the result of a migration of an earlier tale.

No one would deny that along with diffusions of culture there must have gone migrations of myths and symbols.[1] But the difficulty with this theory is that it fails to account for the first version of the mimeographed copies which were later spread abroad. We need a more fundamental explanation of the presence of these common and universal elements in the various religions. This explanation is to be found in the similarity of psychic motivation. Thus, in dealing with the universal practise of the worship of the personified forces of nature, and of sacrifices to the gods, it seems more reasonable to regard these cultural homologies as arising out of the "psychic unity" of mankind than to regard them as plagiarisms from a common historical source. So far as "saviors" are concerned, it would not be difficult to find suggestions which would throw light upon the psychic motivation of the belief in redeemers. The importance of the "Messianic hope" in the creation of Christianity is well known. Undoubtedly the impulse to "hero worship" has played a rôle in the spread of this religion. The existence of such psychic compulsions leads us to conclude that religion is grounded in the psycho-biological make-up of human nature.

There is a feeling that such an analysis of religion destroys its value and sanctity. This, we believe, is false. This idea has its origin in that old fossil of mental evolution that our "animal" nature constitutes the inferior part of our nature. Even if we grant that historically religion originated as a sublimation of the sex instinct (*vide* phallic worship in primitive religion), as the Freudians have it, this need not detract from its present value. The way in which a thing originated, and its present nature as it now functions, are sometimes two entirely dif-

[1] One of the most widespread of these symbols is the swastika, now much in evidence in Nazi Germany. On this and similar points see D. A. Mackenzie's volume, *The Migration of Symbols*.

ferent matters. Soot and a diamond are both made of the same stuff, namely carbon, but how different a diamond is from soot!

Contrary to the view that psychology is hostile to religion we believe that if we are willing to modernize our conception of God we can employ the methods and results of biological psychology in defense of a view of the world which is essentially religious. But the god whom we here propose to substitute for the god of traditional theology may seem a strange god to many. And yet this god alone makes possible the only life we know of; this god is the source of all the energy on earth which sustains man and his institutions. In brief, I wish to argue that *god is light!* And as light god can do all those things which this most remarkable reality of modern physics can accomplish. Moreover, in reply to those who object to this naturalization of god, we will contend that the original God of the Old Testament, and hence the true God of all fundamentalistic Christian doctrine, was at first nothing other than a God of Light. We here take the stand that well nigh all religions in their earlier stages present elements of sun worship, and that most of the analogies of religious thought and inspiration are couched in terms which reflect the sun worship of the early days of religion. Moreover, biological psychology, which is ordinarily thought of as hostile to religion, really issues in a kind of religion which promises a substitute for an outworn theology. In order to make this argument easier to follow it may be indicated that we are aiming at a proof that religion is a transmutation of the form of response in lower organisms known as *positive heliotropism,* and that on the side of biological evolution and religious evolution there is evidence of a movement toward a realization of *vision,* which, starting as a nascent desire to *see,* is eventually sublimated into the spiritual craving which is the soul's quest for *illumination*.

As we have previously noted, this analogy between knowledge and light has been beautifully set forth in Plato's *Republic*. Here the soul is said to be like the eye: it sees those things which are illuminated. Thus we have the analogy of two ruling powers—one set in the intellectual world and the other in the visible. The sun is to visible things as intelligence is to knowledge. This is a fundamental analogy which shows us how dependent we are on the sun, not only for the satisfaction of our material needs but also for the spiritual analogies and inspirations we may have.

II. THE QUEST OF LIFE FOR LIGHT

Theories concerning the origin of religion are as speculative as theories concerning the origin of life. But the theory herein presented has the advantage of linking the explanation of the origin of the one with the explanation of the origin of the other. As we have stated, in order to account for the genesis of religion in naturalistic terms we must be able to find some external stimulus and some internal disposition toward that stimulus. Since sun and star worship are so universal in primitive religion the external cause must be the very presence of these heavenly bodies.[2] The internal predisposition which completes the conditions for the attitude of worship is the tendency to respond sympathetically toward sources of light. This response is known as positive phototropism. But how could religion develop from such a tendency in

[2] For a discussion of the universality of sun worship see Frazer's work, *The Worship of Nature, passim*. On the original sun worship religion in Neolithic times see Hermann Schneider's *History of World Civilization*, Vol. I. See also H. F. Osborn's *Man Rises to Parnassus*.

organisms? And why should it take the form of worship of solar and astral divinities? The answer is simpler than one might expect: Men worship solar gods because sun worship is only a case of what (borrowing a term from acoustics) we may term sympathetic resonance.

It is essential to the present doctrine that light should be recognized as the creative agency in the genesis of living matter. Fortunately there is evidence indicating that light was active in the original synthesis of protoplasm. Just how life originated here on earth is still a mystery, but, as previously pointed out, we may gain some notion of how life may have originated in the shallow seas from the work of E. C. C. Baly on the formation of formaldehyde and the sugars by the action of light of short wave length on carbon dioxide and water. Still more plausibility will accrue to this view when the chemists achieve the photosynthesis of the carbohydrates in the near future.

So much publicity has recently been given to the study of the action of light on living matter that the claim may well be made that light is the long-sought elixir of life. We need hardly make more than passing reference to this evidence. It is known that the exposure of plants and animals to X-rays speeds up the rate of production of mutations, and this tends to lend some indirect confirmation to the claims of Gurwitch concerning "mitogenetic" rays. Again, recent work seems to show that radiations from an electric field, setting up an ionization in the colloidal structure of the ductless glands (producing hormones) may render them more energetic, thus retarding senescence. This method of promoting cellular metabolism is somewhat similar to the process of endowing food with growth-promoting properties by exposure to light, this result being obtained in spite of the fact that the irradiated food, previous to the exposure to light, contained no vitamins. These facts, along with the correlative suggestion that some vitamins are centers of ultra-violet radiation, bear out the conjecture that perhaps in light the modern scientist will find the philosopher's stone, which the older alchemists sought for in some sort of substance. In short, the evidence continues to pile up showing that radiation (light) of one sort or another is always involved in biological processes. All results indicate that light is life, and warmth (when in the infra-red end of the spectrum), and health to man—though death to bacteria. It is in this sense that the sun—the god of primitive man—works miracles, even surpassing those of the "Light of Asia" and the "Light of the World." And the future developments in this field are likely to throw more light on many as yet unsolved biological problems. But we must leave this for the future to unravel.

If light did function in the original synthesis of protoplasm, is it too fantastic to suppose that living systems have retained a biological memory of a cosmic environment with which they aspire to be in tune? And is it too far-fetched to imagine that the longing for union and completion (the "atonement") which characterizes the *illuminati* is but a transfiguration, an alchemy of nature, wherein the "baser" elements of human nature are sublimated into the "nobler" gold of religious aspiration? Such a conception of the incompleteness of human nature seems to me to be less fantastic than the myth of Plato concerning the separation of the sexes. Indeed, the sex impulse (*e.g.*, in the mating of birds) seems to be regulated by the seasonal solar cycle, and a manifestation of it.

Let us suppose that life has retained a memory of the original energy which gave it birth. It is also conceivable that life has preserved an implicit desire to again react in sympathy with the form of radiant energy which cradled it. We may then say that protoplasm has had a constant *desire to see*. This, however, does not commit us to Bergsonian vitalism, for life has a desire to see in the same sense that the moth has a desire for the flame. The desire of the moth is a response *compelled by the stimulus*. In lower organisms these "forced movements" are known as tropisms, and, as stated, the movement of the plant or animal towards the light is known as positive heliotropism. Jacques Loeb, who studied these movements, became a mechanist because, as a result of such studies, he came to the conclusion that the higher forms of response in man could be explained in terms of these tropisms which enslaved him. But here, it seems to me, one of the greatest geniuses of modern science went astray. For by regarding conscious purpose as being simply biological purpose become aware of itself we can assimilate Loeb's theory to the view that evolution is guided along definite lines. The way in which light may have exercised this guidance we now consider.

III. Protoplasmic Memory and Vision

It is generally recognized that in the evolution of organisms old structures will disappear, losing their functions, and new structures will appear with new functions to take the place of the older ones. Thus in the evolution of the nervous system it is known that the lower organisms are dependent upon what are called the "contact senses," such as touch and taste, for their knowledge of the external environment, but that with further specialization the "distance receptors," involving vision and audition, have become more important, eventually assuming dominance over the other senses. In connection with these changes it is important to note that one main difference between man and the lower vertebrates is the extent to which the visual centers in the brain, and the subcortical visual tracts, have developed.

While there is much conflict of opinion in this field, one widely held notion is the distinction which is made between what is called the *old brain* (palæncephalon), which contains the apparatus (the brain stem and cerebellum) necessary for innate, mechanized activities of the reflex type, and the *new brain* (neëncephalon) or cerebral cortex, where are located the individually acquired and relatively variable types of behavior associated with consciousness. It might be argued that this distinction implies that all men really have two souls dwelling in them, as Faust says.

If we adopt this view we then have a dualism: there is the older *animal* soul—identified by some psychoanalysts with man's "subconscious" mind—and the *human* soul, embodying the experiences and ideas peculiar to the individual. It has also been argued by some investigators that the price which human beings have paid for the individual mind is the loss of the hereditary racial mind (or the animal mind with its compelling instincts), while others hold that these "animal" propensities are never completely annihilated, but are normally dominated by the individual mind, and that there is constant danger of reverting to the level of sub-human behavior. If we accept this latter view man then appears as the center of a struggle between two forces: the degrading force of the ancient soul of the animal, and the individual soul of man. Before attempting to determine how these ideas fit into our own view let me restate my thesis.

With regard to the influence of light, if it be true that

wave trains of radiation were active in the primal synthesis of the organic colloids (protoplasms), we may suppose that life has retained a memory of this energy which nourished it. And insofar as developing life is influenced by earlier conditions we may further assume that life has retained a tendency to respond sympathetically to that type of stimulus. If such a hereditary memory can be called a racial heritage in man, we may argue that in him there is an innate tendency to subjugate himself to that type of stimulus which enslaved his biological ancestors. That is, a force from the rear, so to speak, drove man in the direction of sun and star worship.

That such a hereditary memory existed in our primitive ancestors seems to be in accord with the neurological evidence indicating that the processes going on in the upper levels of the nervous system, and therefore in the phylogenetically more recent additions, are influenced in their passage through the lower subcortical levels. Any response is a function of the total gradient of neuronic resistance in the sense that every response has, as it were, secured the permission of all other levels and centers. This does not seem to me to contradict the facts underlying the much discussed "complexes," "conflicts," and "repressions."

While there is this process whereby the past has laid its hands upon future lines of growth, there is also the complementary process whereby the future has reached back, so to speak, and touched hands with the developing present. That is to say, while religion has come into existence as a fulfillment of biological impulses, and to that extent is an expression of a push from the rear, a *vis a tergo*, it has also developed because it is a manifestation of an aspiration upward and toward the future —a *vis a fronté*. Every organism in a sense represents the intersection of the "cone" of the past and the "cone" of the future. Primitive man is in the intermediate stage where the transition from the animal mind to the human soul is being effected. If the transition is to be made safely there must be some continuity of meaning and purpose between the old world which is passing away and the new world which is coming into being. Religion represents the compromise which enables primitive man to make the transition from the world of the animal mind to the new world of unfolding science. Religion is primitive man's way of unifying personality. In support of this view the neurological evidence may again be appealed to.

We are told by the physiologists that the vertebrate eye is an outgrowth of the brain. This has always presented a mystery to the biologist. Vision in invertebrates might be supposed to result from the fact that light, beating down for ages upon unorganized matter, finally modified the outer membrane of the organism in such a way that a sense organ capable of responding to light was differentiated. Thus the pigment spot which enables the simpler invertebrates to see might have been produced in this way. But this, without some supplementary ideas, cannot explain the eye of the vertebrate, for *in the embryonic development of the vertebrate eye the optic stalk develops from the brain itself and grows outward toward the light*. However, if we recall that in embryological development we have an infolding (or invagination) of the ectoderm to form the neural tube, all we need to assume is that the nervous system thus produced retains a memory of its former outer environment of radiant energy. The outward folding (or evagination) of the cerebrum, prolonged into the optic cup which reaches the external world, is to be explained by the supposition that the tissues concerned are again trying to be stimulated by the energy which protoplasm was originally sensitized to. It is for this reason, we suggest, that the optic stalk grows towards the light.[3] This is what is meant by the statement that life has had a desire to see; it is literally true that we want more light!

Perhaps it is for this reason that we have a fear of darkness. The apparent exceptions to this rule of a dislike of darkness might be explained away as a result principally from fatigue with daylight. It is true, of course, that all organisms are not positively heliotropic. Not a few animals are nocturnal, or negatively heliotropic, and seem to fear the light. But this need not upset our theory. We then argue that an animal which shuns the light can never rise to the heights of religious fervor.

In primitive man this fear of darkness was probably more highly developed than in contemporary civilized man. Primitive man's dependence upon the forces of nature is much more direct and obvious than our own. He lived in constant fear of the harmful forces residing in the darkness and the cold of night, which crept upon him as he sat before his flickering fire. The rising sun naturally symbolized the banishing of the forces of evil.

[3] In defense of the view that organisms have had a desire to see, and as the physiological basis of this biological foresight, I suggest the important doctrine of neurobiotaxis. According to Kappers' theory the developing neuroblasts grow towards those regions from which the largest number of excitations come. This means that the developing neuroblast is polarized, and that the axons of the neurones grow outward. Now it seems to me something more than a biological accident that the "growth potentials" or "physiological gradients" which control ontogenetic development should guide the evolution of the visual apparatus in the direction from which, later on, the visual stimuli of a mature organism are to come. In connection with the doctrine of neurobiotaxis I may say that Mrs. Ladd-Franklin once wrote me that Dr. Kappers had exhibited much interest in Dr. Ladd-Franklin's thesis that nerve fibers, when excited, give off light. Mrs. Ladd-Franklin also believed that the investigations in the field of "mitogenetic rays" would confirm her thesis, whether or not it substantiated and helped explain the process of neurobiotaxis.

If it is true, as Lucretius remarked, that in the beginning fear created the gods, then it is not surprising that the sun should become the solar god to whom gratitude and worship are due. It is natural, therefore, that the ancient Greeks should greet with dances and sacrifices the return of the sun which brought spring. These festivals later developed into classical Greek tragedy. But quite universally primitive peoples must have greeted the return of the sun with the same thankfulness which the tortured patient in the hospital experiences when finally, after a long night of waiting, the first grey streaks of dawn project their fingers across the world. And perhaps in us the sadness and melancholy of autumn, of which the poets write, are but a racial heritage or memory associated with the depressed metabolism of animals whose ancestors, with the coming of winter, crawled into holes, retiring into the dark places until the sun of a warmer spring again brought them back to exuberant life.

IV. The Chemistry of Sun Worship

At this point, and in order to soften the effect of what may appear to be the materialistic implications of this theory of the origin of religion, it is desirable to trace some similarities between the present ideas and the theories of a poet and a philosopher who has never been suspected of any sympathy with materialism. I refer here to Goethe, whose *Treatise on Color* (*Zur Farbenlehre*) has been somewhat neglected because the theory of light and color therein presented did not appeal to scientists already persuaded of the essential truth of Newton's theory of light.

"Colors," says Goethe, "are the deeds of light and the sufferings of light." This idea recalls the passage in *Faust*: "Man has his life in light's refracted color." This view of Goethe seems to imply the mystical doctrine that every recipient of light must become a giver of light. Indeed, it might be argued that Goethe's conception is to some extent an anticipation of Bergson's doctrine that the eye was developed as an organ of vision because the organism had a desire to see. In Goethe's view the eye owes its existence to light. Out of indifferent animal organs the light develops an organ of its own likeness; thus the eye forms itself through the light for the light, *in order that the light from within may meet the light from without.*

Is this not only another way of saying that ever since the birth of living matter, a birth having its biparental origin in a fertile photosynthesis of the sun's energy with the carbon compounds of the earth, protoplasm has retained a memory of the cosmic environment of radiation in which we live and move and have our being? The unconscious memory of our subordination to the type of frequency we call light, plus a conscious recognition of the sun's beneficent powers, produced in primitive man a gratitude which makes astral worship inevitable. In so far as religion is an expression of the tendency of living forms to subjugate themselves to light, to that extent it is comparable to the phenomenon of "resonance" or "forced vibration."

According to this view, biological evolution is an expression of the tendency of the cosmic environment of radiant energy to build up in organisms sensitized sounding boards capable of responding to the various frequencies and rhythms of nature. Man's soul grows with his expanding environment. The fact that protoplasm adapts itself so as to serve as a resonator for the wider environment can readily be seen in the case of vision. The brain and the eye, evolving together, have produced a mechanism capable of including a wide purview of the space within the visual field of the two retinæ. Not only is this true of the individual organism, as Professor Kurt Koffka has pointed out in connection with the law of "greatest horopter," but it is also true in the phylogenetic series. Man, the space eater, is lord of creation by virtue of the dominance of vision. It is an important principle which Professor Köhler enunciates when he shows that the adaptive movement of convergence and accommodation illustrate the tendency toward a "closure"—a closure which comes to a termination when the configurative energy of the system reaches a minimum. This explanation of the adaptive responses in vision is stated in terms of the second law of thermodynamics. In another connection this law was summed up by Dr. A. P. Mathews, in his treatise on *Physiological Chemistry* (p. 251), as follows: "Chemical reactions take place in the direction of doing the maximum of external work. This is simply another way of saying that the reaction is always in such a direction that the total potential energy of the system reacting is reduced to a minimum; in other words, the reaction as a whole, but not necessarily in all its parts, always goes in the direction of greater stability under the conditions of the reaction." As previously pointed out, our own way of stating the biological application of this principle would be that the evolutionary processes of nature conspire to arrange the structural configurations in the brain in such a way that the resulting dynamical patterns are capable of dissipating the maximum of potential energy flowing into the organism.

V. Biology and Palæopsychology

Since the time I first presented the foregoing ideas I have become acquainted with the somewhat similar views advocated by Dr. Smith Ely Jelliffe. He approaches the interpretation of human nature from a somewhat different angle. I present his views because, at some points, they appear to lend support to the foregoing interpretation.[4]

Dr. Jelliffe has been mainly interested in the explanation of the behavior of individuals usually classified as "psychotic." Extensive studies made upon such persons has thrown a clearer and more penetrating light into the hidden mechanisms of the normal human mind, for the clues to the unconscious motivations of normal beliefs and action are sometimes most easily discerned in their extreme (pathological) manifestations. Psychoanalysis takes advantage of the "test boring" into the abysses of the inner life and from the facts thus revealed formulates interpretations, hypothetical schematisms concerning the bodily mechanisms underlying the operations of the conscious and subconscious mind.

The behavior of human individuals is always difficult to understand. This is largely because the behavior under consideration is a synthesis of many patterns, some old and some new. The behavior emerges as a whole, apparently undecipherable and unanalyzable. It is this mutual interaction of the parts with each other and with the whole which makes the analysis difficult, especially

[4] At this point I am indebted to the following articles by Dr. Jelliffe: "The Symbol as an Energy Container," *J. of Ner. & Ment. Dis.*, 1919, Vol. 50, 540-550; "Palæpsychology," *Psychoanal. Rev.*, 1923, Vol. 10, 121-139; "On Eidetic Psychology and Psychiatric Problems," *Med. J. & Record*, 1928, 1-12; "Vigilance, the Motor Pattern and Inner Meaning in Some Schizophrenic Behavior," *Psychoanal. Rev.*, 1930, Vol. 17, 305-350.

since the physiological patterns and mental life are so closely intertwined.

If one follows up the implications of the amalgamation of the mental and the physiological, it is natural to consider that the functioning of the body depends upon the way in which it is constructed, and that this, in turn, is an expression of the way in which that body has been structuralized through functional activity in the past. That is to say, the body, as an arrangement of organs and tissues, represents a structuralized record of previous phylogenetic history. The human body is enregistered; it contains a physiological memory of previous activities and experiences. These experiences leave their impress as unconscious gestalten, engram patterns, or phyletic memories.

There is a long and subtly connected chain leading from each individual back into the past. Running forward from this remote past to the present, from the simplest and most primitive organisms to the human race of today, we observe a gradually accumulating combination of engraphic patterns which, beginning with biochemical responses, passes through reflex actions and simple motor responses, to achieve finally, in higher animals, the level of intellectual activity. This latter is made possible through the freeing of the hands, and is a displacement of productive energy from manual activity and facial musculature activity into thought as a symbolic substitute for bodily activity. Thus the mature human individual of today is an accumulation of "memories"; in him there is preserved the story of evolution; the strata of mental life reach back into the more primitive levels of racial and animal behavior.

Dr. Jelliffe, like other investigators, realizes that the body is an organization of dynamically interacting parts, and that the human body, like all living matter, is an energy system for the capture, transformation, and release of energy. Specific organs have been evolved for the capture of cosmic energy; definite organs have been structuralized to handle the incoming energy and transform it, so that effector organs of varying degrees of complexity may discharge it.

For the adequate understanding of the psychology of the individual it thus becomes necessary to possess a thorough knowledge of evolutionary biology. In the human being these evolutionary stages are represented by such levels of response as the cortico-diencephalic-vegetative chain, the cortico-pyramidal-striatal chains, and the fronto-cortical-association chains, which latter exercise the Freudian "repressions" controlling the actions taking place on the lower levels of the hierarchy. Thus these engram patterns are modified by a diversity of energy disturbances at different levels, so that while the conscious brain exercises a "vigilance" over the lower reflexes, these, in turn, modify and determine conscious patterns.

There are various ways of filtering out the strata in order to pair off the various functional activities with their correlative structural bases. Biochemical studies of the relation of tonus to calcium metabolism; anatomical investigations of the phylogeny of the motor apparatus; the study of the hierarchy of behavior patterns; the psycho-sociological study of individual and group responses—all these contribute rich material to this study. It is obvious that from this point of view the transition from psychology to biochemistry is easy and natural. Dr. Jelliffe suggests, for example, that the depletion of the alkali reserves of the body alters the resistance threshold to stimuli, which may result in increased eidetic imagery, or even epileptic motor discharge. This phenomenon is of great significance, as those who have followed the literature on eidetic imagery will recognize. Eidetic images, as we have previously noted, are "seen" by certain types of individuals, though the phenomenon is commonest among children and primitive people. These images, while they are nothing but visualized ideas, are not memory images or visual after-images, for, as pictures, they have all the sharpness of hallucinatory images.

The possible significance of this phenomenon for our theory of religion may now be indicated. From the statement made by E. R. Jaensch, that it is highly probable that in prehistoric periods and in primitive races eidetic images in adults have been more frequent, we may suppose that their presence among moderns represents a kind of psychological atavism, giving us a clue to the history of the gradual synthesis of present human personality. In this respect, as Dr. Jelliffe points out, the phenomenon is parallel to the symptoms of the splitting of personality involving a psychic regression. Another investigator, P. Schilder, has called attention to the fact that eidetic images correspond almost exactly with the perceptions of patients who have suffered from occipital lobe injuries. And following up this idea, we are led through a somewhat roundabout path back to religion.

In his monumental work, *"The Golden Bough,"* Sir James Frazer undertakes an anthropologic and ethnologic study of the ethical aspects of primitive cultural activities. In this study *ritual* stands out as a dominating factor. This controlling principle is similar to what the present-day psychologist calls a compulsion activity. A "compulsion" is a fixed pattern of response. Such patterns of energy discharge are illustrated by the inability to forget melodies, the annoying recall and repetition of verses, the impulse to walk a crack, etc. Such compulsions exist at all levels, and may be traced through physical, chemical, biologic and psychologic to sociologic patterns of action, including here the highest social ritualizations of mankind.

One of the most interesting of these compulsion activities is what is known as the Oculogyric Crisis.[5] In such an attack the eyes sometimes move to an extreme position toward or away from some actual or imagined ("symbolic") object. Frequently the eyes turn upward so that only the whites show, and there may remain in a state of paralysis until the attack is over. In these attacks there is usually an emotional state of anxious compulsion, while the thought movement is slowed up. In his studies Dr. Jelliffe notes many parallels between this attack and certain phenomena of the more abnormal sort in religion. He intimates that the religious phenomena of ecstasy and devotion, and such supernormal phenomena as "possession," are parallel to oculogyric compulsions, coming from within (*i.e.*, the unconscious) rather than from without. In the case of the Delphian ceremony, where the "virgin" awaits possession, she passes through states which indicate a regression: the divine mania here is nothing but an attack of grand hysteria, with eyes rolling convulsively toward the skies. These facts may be of significance when taken in connection with what the records show, namely, that "there are a number of definite indications of the emergence of related primitive impulses; primitive in the sense of the gradual building up of ethical attitudes toward

[5] Here I am indebted to Dr. Jelliffe's paper, "Psychologic Components in Postencephalitic Oculogyric Crises," *Archives of Neurology and Psychiatry*, Vol. 21, 1929, 491-532.

earlier unlicensed anti-social activities in which the 'sense of guilt' serves as the policeman, *i.e.*, the super ego or ideal ego of Freud.

"In short, the song of the psalmist—'Lift up thine eyes to the hills whence cometh thy help'—in the sense of an ethical compulsory substitute for the emergence into consciousness of repressed tabooed wishes—is the primitive, positive level in ethical structure which has built up civilization and culture, and which brings about these movements in the main."

The interconnection between these diverse phenomena is still somewhat obscure, but in confirmation of our own thesis they may be pictured as follows: Man as an organism is a biological reservoir of potentialities, a center of energies seeking an outlet. But man has also, through the evolutionary process, been developed into a social creature, and as a member of society he must learn to repress his selfish impulses so that they conform to the social patterns. Alongside the impulses which release energies quite independent of any reference to cultural patterns there has grown up, through necessity, a tendency to subjugate the self to external social conditions and realities. In this respect the social impulse is analogous to such forced movements as heliotropism. Both compulsory forms of response are manifestations of the form of behavior which William McDougall attributes to the instinct of self-abasement. It is for this reason that the emotion of fear, and the sentiments of awe and reverence, form such important constituent notes in that larger harmony which is called the religious consciousness.

At the most primitive level of organic life the connection between the stimulus and response is direct and immediate. But with increasing complexity of organismic structure and environment this connection grows more remote and indirect. Social stimuli, through substitution, come in time to release the reaction earlier evoked directly by the formative stimuli which helped to build up those reactions. With the coming of human group life and a mechanism of social heredity, the *symbol* begins to function. The symbol is a substitute stimulus, and as a social product it becomes somewhat arbitrary, in the sense that if a person is educated in the proper way any sound or visual image (idol) can acquire the power to elicit those biological responses which are innate in all human organisms. The effectiveness of the religious symbol (idol) rests on its power to evoke a response which provides an outlet for those compulsory reactions of fear, reverence, subordination, etc., which, especially in primitive religion, dominate human nature.

The original tendency toward astral worship reappears under social control through such notions as that heaven is "above," that the gods sit "on high," that the attitude of reverence is one in which the head is "bowed," and that we must "look up" for guidance and "light." Thus the sense of guilt, fundamental to the phenomenon of religious conversion, and the consequent need for purification and redemption, are a kind of reverberation, through a set of socially established symbols, of an original biological instinct in which these symbols did not originally play a part. Perhaps this "looking upward" to heaven and to god, which appears in its purest form in primitive sun worship, manifests itself today in abnormal form in what Dr. Jelliffe terms the "religious expiatory movement of the eyes." These are connected with the sense of guilt previously mentioned and may represent in the present-day individual a recognition of "sin" and a need for punishment. In this respect these oculogyric crises resemble eidetic imagery, both being survivals or phyletic heritages which most contemporary individuals have repressed. The mind, like the body, has its vestigial structures. In its mental development the child may recapitulate some of these earlier racial experiences. Deep in all of us lies that unconscious reservoir of memories which today is covered over by the individually acquired experiences and inhibitions of the conscious mind. Thus palæpsychology gives us a clue to human nature of the present, and the regressions of abnormal personalities today throw light upon the racial integration of human personality.

VI. CHRISTIANITY AND MYTHOLOGY

It now remains for us to show that there is evidence indicating that the religion of the Hebrews, as set forth in the Old Testament, did grow from the same roots of sun worship as other religions. If we reject the supernatural theory of the origin of the religion of Judaism, we must show that the Jehovah of the ancient Jews was a sun god. In opposition to the view that Judaism originated in astral worship, critics of this view will point out that we are told in the book of *Genesis* that God said, "Let there be Light!" and from this it is evident that light was considered to be but a derivative or secondary manifestation of a Being existent previous to the birth of light. This distinction is undoubtedly made, but in reply it may well be argued that it was made after the Jews had passed beyond certain earlier stages of their religious evolution.

There are certain positive reasons for believing that the early Hebrews were given to the worship of the sun, stars, and planets. Thus in II *Kings,* xxiii, 5, we find the prophet enjoining the Jews against this type of worship. This surely means that the spiritual leaders had already made the transition from the worship of the forces of nature which the people *en masse* had not yet made. Exactly the same transition was made in Zoroastrianism, and it has been argued by some scholars that the Jewish (and later Christian) dualism of a power of righteousness, identified with Jehovah, and a power of evil or darkness, personified in Satan, is but a reflection of the Persian ethical dualism in which a God of Light (Ahura Mazda or Ormuzd) struggles against the power of Darkness or Ahrimanes. Some investigators have attempted to show that Zoroastrianism borrowed from Judaism, and others have argued that Judaism borrowed from Zoroastrianism. It appears that this dispute might be settled by showing that this similarity resulted from the fact that both borrowed from a common historical source, which goes back to the earliest symbolic myths common to both branches of the Aryan stock, the Indians and the Iranians.

In connection with the origin of the religion of the Israelites it is interesting to compare the present view with that set forth by James H. Breasted in his study, *The Dawn of Conscience*. Professor Breasted has proposed another, though not inconsistent, account of the highest ethical teachings which theology has credited to the peculiar genius of the ancient Hebrews. He holds that it is a derivative of ancient Egyptian sources, reflecting the substitution of the Egyptian solar religion for the original magical religion. If it is true that conscience, the challenge of the voice within, dawned in the valley of the Nile some five thousand years B.C., then the moral sentiments of civilized society originated in Egypt long before the "age of revelation" of the Hebrews. This monistic belief reaches its culmination in the reformation of Akhenaton, who substituted the worship of the sun god in the place of polytheism. This view of Professor Breasted has one advantage over our own version, in that it then is possible to make connections with the New Testament through the Greek *Logos* doctrine. This *Logos* doctrine appears in Christian form in the *Gospel of John* in the statement, "In the beginning was the Word, . . . etc." From this point of view, as A. E. Avey has pointed out, the *Logos* doctrine of the Grecizing Christians is a diffusion of culture from the religion of the sun of the land of ancient Egypt. And that is still quite in harmony with our own theory of the origin of religion.

ADDENDUM

Among the interested persons who have expressed an opinion on the foregoing theory of the origin of religion is Professor Hudson Hoagland. In commenting on the theory Hoagland states that he believes that one could make out a better case for geotropism than phototropism. He states: To say that an animal is either positively or negatively phototropic is simply to say that it orients until the intensity of excitation on the two sides of its central nervous system are equal. As Loeb points out, this is a forced movement until equality of bilateral excitation is established. Hence, we ask, why not impute to religion as a basis the attempt to "orient" oneself so as to follow the "straight and narrow path," and to "avoid temptation" (*i.e.*, to reduce random movements to a minimum)? If we add to this the fact that by far most animals are negatively geotropic—*i.e.*, they climb *up* against gravity until the tension of the muscles on the two sides of the body are equal and hence the bilateral brain fields are equally excited—we have the biological basis of the "upward striving" of the religious person and perhaps the basis of the notion of heaven being in the sky as a final goal of life's striving.

I am not entirely certain that Professor Hoagland is serious in making this suggestion, but taking it thus my only comment here is that perhaps negative geotropism is only another name for positive heliotropism. When a plant grows *upward* is it growing *away* from the attraction of gravity or is it growing *toward* the source of light? Does it make much difference how we state this fact, so long, at least, as the two are inseparable?

PART II

PHILOSOPHY AND THE SOCIAL SCIENCES

CHAPTER X

HISTORY AND ETHICS

I. Is a Science of Social Change Possible?

To THE individual untutored in the art of intellectual synthesis the field of history is a welter of detached facts and chaotic episodes. To such a person there appears to be little meaning to the processes of history. But the scientist, the philosophical historian, cannot rest satisfied with such an attitude. In the mind which seeks the unity underlying multiplicity there exists an impelling demand for some formula, some general equation, exhibiting the coherence believed to underlie these seemingly unrelated facts.

Attempts at a philosophy of history have not been lacking. The desire to bring order out of chaos by subsuming the minutiæ of social change under the descriptive or explanatory formulæ of a science or philosophy of history has lured more than one theorist into the province of speculation. Accordingly, we have seen the rise of various "interpretations" of history: the spiritual interpretation of St. Augustine in his *City of God;* Hegel's imposing conception, which rose and fell in a manner exemplifying his own dialectical movement; the hardly less enterprising systems of Auguste Comte and Herbert Spencer; and, finally, the sweeping, not to say devastating, morphology of history of Spengler. But we still await the appearance of a system that will recommend itself equally to the social scientist and the philosopher. The record of past failures suggests the difficulty of the undertaking, and rash indeed is he who invades this domain in the belief that the hunting is good.

If, therefore, one approaches this subject in a constructive spirit, he should be sensitive to the difficulties and informed in advance of the likelihood of failure. But today the philosopher of history has at least one initial advantage, in that he can, if he is circumspect, see and perhaps avoid some of the mistakes of his predecessors. It is also clear that any system which is to be true to the spirit of the times must give due weight to the important rôle which so-called economic and material factors have played in the processes of social change. These factors, it is now believed, are no less potent as causal agents than the so-called spiritual aspirations and rational determinations of individuals and social groups. It is now commonly asserted by social scientists that in the past the importance of economic, geographic, and climatic factors in molding the actions of men and the fates of nations has been all too frequently underestimated. Needless to say, contemporary social scientists are trying to correct this one-sidedness.

This very movement of thought in social science, away from the idealistic towards the materialistic interpretation, is reminiscent of the first two movements of the Hegelian dialectic, the thesis and the antithesis. Perhaps this similarity is not accidental, for it will be recalled that the materialistic interpretation of Karl Marx was but an inversion of the idealistic formula of Hegel. Thus through the reaction of the left wing of the Hegelian school, in the form of the materialism of Feuerbach, Engels, and Marx, there was brought into existence the movement which was to supplant in a considerable meas-

ure the original idealism out of which it grew. Whatever
other implications one may see in this turn of events, it
is at least clear that the evolution of scientific thought
itself now appears to follow a pattern which is quite as
lawful as the evolution of living organisms. The spirit of
modern social science is what might have been anticipated, for it is a reaction against the extreme form of
the intellectualistic interpretation of Hegel. Furthermore, the present uncertain status of the problem represents the inevitable juncture in the onward movement of
scientific interpretation. The social scientists are groping
for principles, and cannot yet envisage the outlines of
the third movement of the Hegelian dialectic, the synthesis, which is to harmonize the idealistic and the materialistic interpretations. In order to explain and justify
this statement it is necessary to enter upon a brief general survey of the development of the sciences during
the last few centuries.

Since the origin of science out of the magic and sorcery
of primitive tribal life, science has moved in one general
direction. It is said that if you give the astronomer two
observations on the path of a comet he can reconstruct
the total trajectory and state whether this path is an
ellipse, or a parabola, or an hyperbola. In the same way,
if we make several observations on various stages of the
evolution of the sciences we can detect a general drift in
the curve of scientific thought. Plotting the arc, we find
that the one general direction in which scientific thought
bends is (a) towards an ever-increasing exclusion of the
capricious, the miraculous, and supernatural powers or
agencies, and (b) in the direction of a greater reliance
upon the use of empirical method, towards the discovery
and summary of observed facts in the form of uniform
laws of behavior of the entities studied. As a result of

this evolution we now find that present theories stand in striking contrast to the older theories of natural processes. This contrast now appears to hold in the social sciences no less than in the several branches of natural science.

The older theory of history bears one striking resemblance to the old theory of geological processes: both were based on the idea that sudden changes were initiated through the intervention of a supernatural power. The theory of Divine Providence, that the course of natural events could be suspended while God worked a miracle, is an exact parallel to the explanation of human history in terms of supernatural catastrophic agencies. And just as geology became a science by adopting the hypothesis of *uniformitarianism*—the theory that the forces now at work are identical in nature with those which produced changes in past ages—so the phenomena of society have lent themselves to scientific study in the measure that the same uniformitarian doctrine has been adopted by social science. In both fields it is now held that the present is the clue to the past, and the past contains the explanation of the present.

One of the most remarkable phenomenon in modern times is the rapid development of a science of society which has followed upon the acceptance of the uniformitarian theory. The social sciences hardly existed prior to Spencer and Comte, though there had, to be sure, been adumbrations of the scientific study of mankind in earlier times. It is a remarkable fact that many of the men who have contributed much to this movement are almost contemporaneous with our generation.

Within the course of several generations a surprising amount of factual material concerning the structure and evolution of society has been amassed. Of course, when it comes to the interpretation of this data, to the drawing of general conclusions from the results of these studies, especially the more recent statistical data, not much of importance has been accomplished. But this is not taken as grounds for discouragement by most students. The fact is that the social sciences must study as their units human individuals and social groups, thus introducing all the problems of individual and social psychology, and since this latter discipline can at present hardly be regarded as a science—being now only the hope of a science, as William James said—it is surely not to be expected that the other youthful but lusty social sciences could achieve results comparable to those now incorporated in the body of the older physical sciences. Social science is at present characterized by the absence of prediction and control of the phenomena it studies.

Social scientists are on the whole by no means discouraged with their results. They are at least as much agreed in their belief that a science of society is possible as the psychologists are agreed that a science of human nature is possible. The problem of the social scientist is how to formulate the fundamentals of such a science. Sociology, economics, and political science are making tentative steps towards hypotheses which will provide satisfactory working principles for a science of man in society. They are reaching towards the formulation of unifying and explanatory generalizations comparable to the great unifying principles of physical science, such as Newton's laws of motion and the two great laws of energetics.

Several attempts have been made to crystallize the principles for such a discipline. Some of these formulations are curious, indicating the extremes to which an investigator will go to find a neat formula to cover the conglomeration of facts. In general these attempts at a social science have taken their cue from the more respected physical sciences. The advocates of this type of social science point to the historical evolution of science as affording support to their view. They point out, what we have already noted, that primitive man was anthropomorphic, and therefore arrived at an animistic explanation of the phenomena of nature. They then point out that, beginning with the external world, the animistic purposive, and humanly arbitrary elements have progressively been expelled. This movement to cast out the spirits and devils from nature began in astronomy and physics, and later extended itself into the biological sciences. Our positivists of social science therefore conclude that further progress depends upon a further extension of this method and point of view, assuming without much question that the methodology which has proven so fertile in the "lower" sciences can be no less fruitful in the "higher" sciences. Hence we now find man, the last citadel of vitalism and purpose, being included within the scope of the onward sweep of the "mechanistic" viewpoint. It is for this reason that some social scientists have recently attempted to develop behavioristic sociologies, behavioristic theories of law, industry, and so on.

In justice to the facts it must be pointed out that some of these theorists who are introducing physical conceptions and methods into the social sciences are not "behaviorists." Nevertheless, they are in and of the same general current which is carrying the behaviorists along. An instance will suffice to illustrate the point. One of the most interesting lines of thought directed towards formulating the fundamentals of a science of society is presented in the conceptions of the European sociologist,

Wilfredo Pareto, who, in his *Traité de Sociologie Generale,* argues that the methods of mathematics and the physical sciences can be carried over into the social sciences. Pareto regards human society as analogous to a system of molecules undergoing various combinations in space and time. Some critics might like to raise the question of how it is that if we, as individuals, correspond to the molecules of a gas we can know anything of the total state. That is, as constituents of a statistical ensemble we see what happens within the system, but only a super-observer could note from without those changing combinations which constitute the cultural patterns. The impossibility of such a human super-observer would seem to place a limitation upon the possibility of a science based on such assumptions.

During the course of the development of the foregoing ideas the ethicist has not remained an indifferent spectator. It is obvious that a movement towards the physicizing of social phenomena, since it has so many adherents, cannot be without considerable significance. For the most part, ethicists of the older school have looked askance at the exuberance of the enthusiastic apostles of mechanistic explanation. These idealists, frequently exponents of the armchair method of investigation, refer to this development as an *aping* of the physical sciences. They may refer to the *growing pains* of the adolescent social sciences in even less flattering terms. The reason for their protest apparently lies in the fear that spiritual values will suffer if the scope of mechanistic explanation is extended to include the domain of human relationships. They reiterate that "man does not live by bread alone"; that we must not "throw out the baby with the bath"; that no race of men has ever been satisfied with

226 PHILOSOPHY AND THE SOCIAL SCIENCES

materialism; that conditioned reflexes are not the whole
of human behavior. These are some of the warnings and
pronunciamientos sounded from time to time by the
idealists.

It is difficult to discover just what the truth in these
matters may be. It is undoubtedly a fact that ethical
theory and practical morality are changing. But it is more
difficult to see how it can be shown that they are changing for the worse. And even though we are degenerating
morally, is this necessarily due to the influence of the increasing popularity of materialistic psychology and mechanistic sociology? In the present situation it is well to
keep in mind that ever since the time of Socrates (and
probably long before) men have been persecuted for
"corrupting" the youth and for introducing "false divinities." If this can teach us anything it probably is that
there is no justification for the fear that a "scientific"
theory of human nature and society will upset the foundations of morality.

At this point some ethicists are likely to call a halt, in
order to point out that we must not assume without
proof that the business of ethics is to preach. Advocates
of this view may insist that ethics is a *descriptive* science
(like biology) and not a *normative* science. This situation calls to mind the difference of opinion among philosophers concerning the nature and function of their
subject, and raises a fundamental point which must be
considered.

II. FACTS AND IDEALS

In considering the question of what mission, if any,
philosophy has in this world two conceptions of the function of philosophy appear. According to one conception,

the proper attitude of a philosopher should be that of the disinterested observer of the world's history and the vicissitudes of the cosmic process. The philosophical attitude is that of the detached and dispassionate onlooker of the tragi-comedy of life. This attitude is illustrated in a measure by the calm and dignity of the mature Goethe, who, throughout the agitation in politics which followed the spread of Rousseau's romantic social theories and the dissemination of the spirit of the French revolution, refused to align himself with any political party or social movement. Such an attitude is also simulated by those disillusioned cynics who believe that there are already too many reformers who think they know what is wrong with the world and how to set it right. What we need, the spectator-philosopher might say, is a fraternity of unbelievers in reform, skeptics who have faith in no nostrums or panaceas.

The other view of the nature and function of philosophy is that philosophy *does* have a practical mission in the life of society. As we have seen, this is the view of John Dewey, who for many years has seen in an enlightened education the prime instrument of social reconstruction. This is also the attitude of H. G. Wells, who every year has a new medicine to cure the ills of the social order; as often as civilization can be wrecked, so often can Mr. Wells salvage it.

In casting about for a way of harmonizing these two divergent attitudes it is necessary to point out at the very outset that no philosopher has ever succeeded in maintaining a lasting and complete neutrality towards the events happening about him, and that all great philosophers have supplemented their purely speculative adventures with some sort of social philosophy. It is true that Plato defined the philosopher as the "spectator of

all time and all existence," but it is no less true that he
also stated that the ills of society would never cease until
philosophers became kings and kings became philosophers. The *reductio ad absurdum* of the ethical neutrality of philosophy is that those who thus regard ethics as a
descriptive science are saying that those who hold to the
opposing view are *wrong*. Since this is itself an ethical
judgment, it shows that the advocates of the descriptive
view are contradicting themselves. After all, the difference between the two views is one of mood or tempera-
ment, and all of us are occasionally in the mood when we
approve what appears to be an act of social intelligence
or condemn what appears to be an act of stupidity.

Having thus justified the right of philosophy to moral-
ize, let us therefore at this point consider the question,
What positive goals for individual conduct and social
evolution can philosophy formulate and present to a perplexed world?

The chaos in the field of ethics is well known to all
who are familiar with the many different types of ethical
theory. This fact has been pointed out in an interesting
way by Jacques Rueff [1] in the following words: "The
reading of a book on ethics is for a scientific mind a
source of profound astonishment. The systems are in-
numerable, the conclusions are unique. Whether the
ethics expounded is religious or utilitarian, finalistic or
pragmatic, it leads always to a well determined set of
rules which are, with small variations, the customary
ethics of our civilized world." In the past this chaos has
frequently been due to the fact that philosophers have
not formulated explicitly their fundamental assumptions and then proceeded to deduce rigidly the consequences of these assumptions or postulates. How can we

---

[1] *Des Sciences physiques aux Sciences morales,* Alcan, Paris, 1922.

hope to coöperate in building up an imposing superstructure of ethics if we don't even have a blue print of our foundations?

In cases where an attempt was made to approach ethics in the manner in which a mathematician approaches his field, the axioms formulated were in most cases unacceptable to others. Various ethicists have indeed tried to set up principles of moral science which would be analogous to the *postulates* (formerly called *axioms*) of Euclidian geometry. As is well known, Spinoza attempted to follow the mathematician's mode of procedure. Descartes was also greatly influenced by the methodology of mathematics. Kant, in his *categorical imperative,* stated that we should always act in such a way that the maxim of our action could be made a universal law. It was as axiomatic to Kant that we should always treat humanity as an end and never as a means as the golden rule is axiomatic to the theoretical ethics of the layman. Hegel had about the same idea when he told us that we should always act as persons and treat others as persons. Among the utilitarians it was argued that a self-evident proposition of ethics is to be found in the principle that the happiness of any one individual is just as important as the happiness of any other.

All of these statements aim at some universal, axiomatic, and self-evident principle, a principle of impartiality or democracy. And yet it is significant that not all experts would accept such a principle of impartiality as a basis for ethics. It remains a brute fact that in the field of morality the principles which seem self-evident and necessary to one expert are not axiomatic to others. It would not be difficult to exhibit difficulties in each of the foregoing propositions—including the famous golden rule—so that none of them can be taken as an axiom for a system of social ethics. This might seem to introduce a discouraging note into an attempt at a mathematical approach to morality. This, however, does not necessarily follow. It is now clear that one of the reasons for the failure of this methodology in the past lay in the fact that these systems were designed to fit a previously conceived set of ethical principles. That is to say, the inability to discover necessary and universally acceptable principles was due in a large measure to the fact that the moralist had at the very outset of his inquiry an idea of what people *ought* to do, and then looked around for principles that would enable him to prove that they *can* do these things because they ought. Axioms are here chosen in order to prove preconceived conclusions. Needless to say, such procedure is not logically sound, and leads to systems of ethics at variance with facts.

It is obvious that this procedure is just the reverse of that followed in a natural science. Any system that does not take into account what human beings actually can do, which ignores man's biological and psychological nature in one respect or another, is bound to fail. One of the best illustrations of this is found in Stoicism, which, in spite of its appeal, failed to survive because its exalted intellectualism was too lofty for the average man, who found it impossible to eradicate his emotional nature as Stoicism advised.

The first serious attempt at a scientific system of ethics came with the utilitarians. Here a definite attempt was made to ground the "ought" in the "is." In asserting that men, *as a matter of fact,* by their very natures are compelled to pursue happiness, thus starting from the basis of *psychological* hedonism, the utilitarians prepare the way for the argument that men *ought* to pursue happiness, and thus consistently come out with the doctrine of *ethical* hedonism. As is well known, this view of social hedonism (as utilitarianism is sometimes called) resembles in some respects the hedonism of the Epicureans, differing from it mainly in the fact that the utilitarians substitute social happiness (the "greatest happiness of the greatest number") for the egoistic pleasure of the Epicureans, or individualistic hedonists.

One interesting phase of the utilitarian movement is the way in which it is used to support the economic theory known as the *laissez faire* doctrine. Since, according to the hedonistic theory, men pursued pleasure and avoided pain, they would always, in their economic activities, act in such a way as to increase their pleasure and decrease the amount of pain and discomfort. Now the activities of men are classified into production of economic goods and the consumption of the same. It was assumed by the utilitarians and the classical economists that as a consumer our "economic" man would purchase those things which would give him the greatest amount of pleasure. He would naturally seek to secure this commodity at the cheapest possible price. The producer, on the other hand, would produce those commodities for which there was the greatest demand, selling his product to the highest bidder. This interaction between production and consumption, selling and buying, was supposed to produce the greatest possible wealth with the least effort and waste. Thus through sheer self-interest the good of the community was supposed to be taken care of. It was supposed by such classical *laissez faire* economists as J. S. Mill and Adam Smith that the best possible society would result if individuals were left alone, since economic laws were in harmony with the utilitarian doctrine of the "good" life.

It is now generally believed that this system of thought

is abandoned once and for all. Criticisms have been launched against it from all sides. From the side of economics, the effects of the industrial revolution showed that industry and commerce, left to themselves, produce anything but social order and well-being. The state has had to interfere more and more in regulating conditions and hours of labor in factories. In this respect, as someone has said, we are all socialists now. From the side of philosophy, it has been argued by many that the psychological basis of the utilitarian theory is unsound. On the one hand, the political realists argue that men are not as rational as the *laissez faire* doctrine assumes. Even if the situation be as simple as the theory of the "economic man" assumes, men do not possess sufficient knowledge or intelligence to secure those things which give individuals the most pleasure and do society the greatest good. Idealists, on the other hand, criticize the doctrine by saying that the theory depreciates and underestimates the rôle of reason in determining man's behavior, and is therefore based upon a false theory of human nature. It is also pointed out that when J. S. Mill introduces a qualitative test in the selection of actions leading to pleasure and states that it is better to be a Socrates dissatisfied than a pig satisfied he is in fact abandoning the hedonistic doctrine.

Thus the first attempt at a scientific approach to social ethics ends in defeat and disaster. While it is true that one well known eugenicist is attempting a revival of utilitarian doctrine in what he calls a neo-Benthamian form, it does not now appear that there is much to be rescued from the wreck of this once impressive system.

It was previously pointed out that the contemporary attempts at formulating a science of man in society have issued in some curious results. We have already noted in passing the interesting doctrine presented by Pareto. Another illustration of the lure of this field is found in the suggestive view formulated by Dr. V. C. Branham,[2] who has attempted to apply the chemical law of mass action to social phenomena. The law of mass action states that the ratio between two or more chemically interacting substances and the products formed by them is a constant, if the reaction is reversible and has reached a state of equilibrium. In more technical form: if

$$A + B \leftrightarrows C + D, \text{ then } \frac{[C] \cdot [D]}{[A] \cdot [B]} = K \text{ (a constant)}$$

This investigator argues that social reactions are prone to reach a state of equilibrium in which the process is reversible and limited to the workings of the mass-action law: the system tends constantly to change because new components of the social process tend to form new combinations which in turn follow mass-action principles.

Another investigator, Dr. A. P. Weiss,[3] goes at the problem from a somewhat different angle. He sees some promise in an application of the minimum energy theory, best formulated by Richard Avenarius in his *Philosophie als Denken der Weltgemaess dem Pricip des kleinsteins Kraft-masses* (Preface, Berlin, 1917). According to Weiss, the behaviorist, the aim of the individual is so to act that the adjustment between the individual and the environment will occur with the least expenditure of energy. The ethical implication of this is said to be as follows: that behavior which contributes most toward

[2] In an article on "The Chemical Mass-Action Law as Applied to Social Adaptation," *Journal of Abnormal and Social Psychology*, 1928, Vol. 23, 72-79.

[3] In a paper on "Behaviorism and Ethics," in the *Journal of Abnormal and Social Psychology*, 1928, Vol. 22, 388-398.

maintaining this normal metabolic rate (or produce a stable physiological equilibrium) will be classified as good, and that which interferes as bad.

In the foregoing conceptions we have a selection from the more stimulating and interesting of the various attempts at a generalization of physical principles so that they become susceptible of biosocial applications. It is not our purpose here to enter into a discussion and criticism of these views. But it may be said that to the present writer these views do not appear to provide a broad basis for a comprehensive social philosophy. It must be granted that more general implications and more detailed applications might be worked out, but this must be undertaken by the inventors of these respective systems.

And now a few words by way of outlining the general features of the doctrine which, it is hoped, will be rendered plausible in the following pages.

In the first place it is well to point out that the conception to be outlined in the following chapters has points in common with the foregoing doctrines. It resembles them in seeking for the origin and terminus of moral action in the world we live in rather than in some transempirical world of a miracle-inspired religion. In this respect the present view may be described as "naturalistic." It must be kept in mind, however, that the term naturalism, as here employed, does not imply materialism. Between the extreme positions of supernaturalism and materialism there surely is some mediating position—a view perhaps to be described by the term "creative morality." The three views just mentioned might be described in terms of the Hegelian dialectic, as follows:

THESIS—*Supernaturalistic morality:* a religion based on revelation and prophecy. Here the source of ethical ideals and principles is supposed to be in another world. The test of the goodness of an act is its imagined correspondence with the eternal and absolute standards of this transcendent world. This doctrine of *two-worldism* involves a *pre-evolutionary* view of man and society.

ANTITHESIS—*Moral scepticism:* an ethics denying the existence of objective (trans-personal) standards of the good life. This individualistic relativism may be based on a theory of knowledge (as in Sophistry), a materialistic metaphysics (such as that of the Epicurean philosophy), or may be a result of an emotional reaction against supernaturalistic religion.

SYNTHESIS—*Creative morality:* an ethics based on the belief in evolution. It asserts that while new (unforeseen) conditions arise calling for new ideas and responses, the moral standards are not relative to the individual. In the emergent evolution of morality there is a definite direction to the process which points to certain super-personal standards.

Any system of ethics which pretends to be naturalistic must find its norms and standards in certain pervasive principles of nature which can be recognized to be at work throughout the evolutionary process. In embracing the view that the function of human social evolution is to bring to efflorescence a process already going on at the lower level of biological evolution we are of course presupposing an analogy between the human social and the strictly biological. Here we look to what has happened in the transition from the chemical to the biological as also affording us a parallel to what must happen in the transition from the biological to the human. In a previous generation the question was debated, Can biological evolution, like chemical reactions, be brought under the scope of natural law? The answer is now given in the affirmative. As Dr. Alfred J. Lotka [4] points out, the science of physical biology proceeds on the assumption that there must be an analogy between biological and chemical evolution, and this is found in the formula that *evolution is the history of a system undergoing irreversible changes.*

In developing the present conception it has been found necessary to revive the organismic theory of society. It follows that if society is an organism, the same laws of energetics must be applicable to the behavior of the developmental processes (the evolution of culture-patterns) of society as are applicable to the similar processes of an individual organism. However, in order to provide a place for the novel elements which appear from time to time the current doctrine of emergent evolution is introduced. It must not be thought that this linkage of the notion of emergent evolution with the idea of organismic patterns involves any clash with the laws of energetics. Rather, as I shall try to show, the second law of thermodynamics, which plays an important rôle in the present theory, is a name for this fact of the emergence of macroscopic states or "social" patterns. It is this law which lies behind the irreversible character of the evolutionary process, a fact which, as Dr. Lotka points out, was stated by Josiah Royce [5] in these words: ". . . the second law of the theory of energy is now generally regarded as essentially a statistical law. So viewed, the second law of energy becomes a principle stated wholly in terms of the theory of probability. It is the law that the physical world tends, in each of its parts, to pass from certain less probable to certain more probable configurations of its moving particles. As thus stated the

[4] *The Elements of Physical Biology,* p. 24.
[5] *Science,* 1914, Vol. 39, p. 551.

second principle . . . becomes a law of evolution." This law, as Royce indicates, is a statistical principle, and it is decidedly the suspicion of modern science that in micro-physical phenomena statistics are producing miracles.

The foregoing statement concerning "miracles" means that the element of novelty, wherever it appears, introduces a limitation to the scientist's power of explanation. Some physicists have the faith that the trouble comes from averaging things, and that the miraculous appearance of a statistical constancy in the aggregate out of what appears to be the indeterminacy of the behavior of the parts (electrons [6]) would disappear if we could consider the individual entities, and not their mean. Our own view, however, is that the macroscopic mean does contain an element of novelty, which results from the dynamic interaction of parts to produce new (social) wholes, and that this process is at work in those statistical ensembles known as human societies. At this point we make contact with the ideas of Dr. A. N. Whitehead, who, in his *Process and Reality*, speaks (p. 151) of molecules as subordinate societies in the society of the living cell, of electrons and protons (p. 152) and crystals as societies, of the "electromagnetic society" (p. 149), of a train of light waves (pp. 53-4) involving a social order, and suggests (p. 142) that the doctrine that order (or as we should say, macroscopic pattern) is a social product appears in modern science in the statistical theory of the laws of nature. According to our own use of the statistical theory, all culture patterns, following the terminology of *gestalt* psychology, may be termed

[6] On this matter of the indeterminacy of the behavior of electrons see P. W. Bridgman's paper "The Recent Change of Attitude Toward the Law of Cause and Effect," *Science*, 1931, Vol. 73, 539-547.

social gestalten. Since a gestalt, as an emergent whole, is something other than the sum of the properties of the constituent parts, it follows that the miracles accomplished by statistical processes must extend to the social life of humans. It must never be forgotten that our usage of the term miracle has nothing in common with its traditional sense. "Creative morality" has little to do with the Calvinistic belief in Divine Providence.

CHAPTER XI

THE ENERGETIC INTERPRETATION OF HISTORY

In ANALYZING the various interpretations of history, the materialistic interpretation, the idealistic interpretation of Hegel, and the "great man" theory of Carlyle and Emerson, we find that none of these explicitly recognize the importance of the one factor on which the entire structure of modern civilization is based, which is *energy!* Energy is the common denominator of the various activities—production, distribution, consumption— of our economic-political order. If, therefore, our interpretation of history is to go to the heart of the problem of social change, it must assign to this ubiquitous physical reality a rôle commensurate with its causal potency in nature and society. Moreover, the energetic interpretation of history has the advantage of being free of association with prejudicial epithets. It is scientific without being materialistic; it represents idealism without supernaturalism, aristocracy without snobbishness, and democracy without degeneration.

The present interpretation is not put forth as an entirely unique and original viewpoint of which there have been no earlier anticipations. As with all scientific hypotheses, there have been adumbrations of the doctrine, though it is to be noted they are all of recent origin. Probably we will not go far wrong if we look to the great German chemist Wilhelm Ostwald for the first articulate suggestions towards such a theory. Ostwald was the out-

standing proponent of the system of physical chemistry
termed *energetics*. In speculating about the wider implications of this view Ostwald naturally considered the
social significance of the doctrine, and presented some
interesting ideas which we shall have occasion to refer to
in subsequent paragraphs. Another theorizer alert to the
possibilities of an energetic interpretation of history was
Henry Adams, and all subsequent investigators must
acknowledge some degree of indebtedness to him. Henry
Adams saw in the second law of thermodynamics (sometimes called the principle of the degradation of energy),
applied to social phenomena, the implication of a degrading tendency in society, a tendency to level down. What
he failed to see was that in organic nature there is also
a process of emergence of new levels of energy which
dominate the behavior of the elements of the lower
levels. A third student of the subject who has glimpsed
the significance of energy in civilization is the economist,
T. N. Carver.[1] Professor Carver argues that the life
processes of social groups consists in transforming the
largest possible sum of solar energy into human energy.
Civilization, he tells us, is a device for storing this
energy, and social welfare depends upon its utilization
in such ways as to increase this sum total of utilization
of the sun's energy.

Another pioneer in this field was the late Dr. Edwin E.
Slosson, who hoped to present an interpretation of history stated in terms of its relation to the second law of
thermodynamics.[2] Unfortunately, the untimely death of
Dr. Slosson prevented the completion of this project.

[1] See his book, *The Economy of Human Energy,* 1924.
[2] The author had some correspondence with Dr. Slosson on this matter. Dr. Slosson had lectured before learned groups on this subject, and
hoped to bring his ideas together in systematic form on some future
occasion. I shall do my best to carry this view a step forward.

According to this great interpreter of science, the reason for the incessant rise and fall of civilizations is to be sought in the dominance which the control of the supplies of energy confer upon nations. Quoting Ostwald, we may say, "The Actual, that is, what acts upon us, is energy." The destinies of men and nations are the record of the actualizations of history through energy domination. This fact is so well stated by Ostwald that we quote his own words in full [3]:

The objective characteristic of progress consists in improved methods of seizing and utilizing the raw energies of nature for human purposes. Thus it was a cultural act when a primitive man discovered that he could extend the radius of his muscle energy by taking a pole in his hand, and it was another cultural act when a primitive man discovered that by throwing a stone he could send his muscle energy a distance of many meters to the desired point. The effect of the knife, the spear, the arrow, and of all the other primitive implements can be called in each case a purposive transformation of energy. And at the other end of the scale of civilization the most abstract scientific discovery, by reason of its generalization and simplification, signifies a corresponding economy of energy for all the coming generations that may have anything to do with the matter. Thus, in fact, the concept of progress as here defined embraces the entire sweep of human endeavor for perfection, or the entire field of culture, and at the same time it shows the great scientific value of the concept of energy.

If we consider further that, according to the second fundamental principle of energetics, the free energy accessible to us can only decrease, but not increase, while the number of men whose existence depends directly upon the consumption of a due amount of free energy is constantly on the increase, then we at once see that objective necessity of the development of civilization in that sense. His foresight puts man in a position to act culturally. But if we examine our present social

[3] From his small book on *Natural Philosophy*.

order from this point of view, we realize with horror how barbarous it still is.

This view has repeatedly been stated in characteristically terse and picturesque sentences by Edwin E. Slosson, who was an admirer of his fellow chemist, Wilhelm Ostwald. According to Dr. Slosson, the history of the world will remain a riddle, an inexplicable succession of chance happenings, until the historian recognizes the importance of chemical factors in the course of human events. To quote his own words [4]:

Wherein is modern civilization superior to ancient civilization and primitive barbarism? In what respects is the man of today ahead of his primitive forebears? Probably not in physique or mentality. . . .

But a man in modern times, even though he may be comparatively weak in body and dull in mind, knows more and can do more than the strongest and brightest men in former times. He knows more because he has at his command the accumulated knowledge of the ages, selected, tested, and arranged for his benefit. He can do more because he can supplement his feeble muscles with engine power. He can travel fifty times as fast, accomplish a hundred times as much work in a day, lift a weight a thousand times as heavy, and make his voice heard ten thousand times as far. Both these advantages, the physical and the intellectual, he owes to chemistry. It is chemistry that has given him the power that runs his engines and the metals that make his machines. It is chemistry that has given him his books—the paper, the ink, the type, the alphabet.

In the last sentence of the quotation Slosson had in mind the fact that the alphabet used nearly all over the world was the invention of the Phœnicians because they needed

---

[4] "The Expansion of Chemistry," *Journal of Industrial and Engineering Chemistry*, 1924, Vol. 16, 447 ff.

it in their business, which was chemical industries (metallurgy, dyeing, glass, etc.) and commerce in chemical commodities.

The chemist is not merely the manipulator of molecules; he is the manager of mankind. His discoveries and inventions, his economies and creations, often transform the conditions of ordinary life, alter the relations of national power, and shift the currents of thought, but these revolutions are effected so quietly that the chemist does not get recognition for what he accomplishes, and, indeed, does not usually realize the extent of his sociological influence. Dr. Slosson likes to elaborate on this theme of chemistry as an agent for democracy. Let us quote his very readable lines [5]:

Chemistry is the most effectual agent for democracy, since it actually accomplishes in regard to many material things that equality which legislation aims to bring about in the political sphere. Luxuries, formerly the monopoly of the privileged classes, become, through applied science, the common property of the masses. The "royal purple" of the ancient dyes far more beautiful are now to be had on the bargain counter, and Solomon in all his glory was not arrayed like the modern American maiden. Even though her purse be scant she need not lack jewels and perfumes and fine raiment such as once were worth a slave's life. In early ages the man who owned a piece of steel shaped it into a sword and made himself master of his fellows. Now we make buildings out of steel and he who lives in the garret of one of them could look down on the tower of Babel. The Feudal Age vanished with the first whiff of gunpowder, for that device of the Black Art leveled the natural and the artificial inequalities of humanity in warfare, since with a gun in his hand the churl could meet the knight on equal footing and the dwarf was match for the giant—more than a match, for

[5] From his paper, "The Human Side of Chemistry," *Journal of Industrial and Engineering Chemistry*, 1922, Vol. 14, 887 ff.

he had the larger target. Medicines such as a prince could not procure, though his physicians surveyed the earth from China to Peru, are now at hand to cure the pauper. The new chemical motive powers have given man in the automobile a very fair substitute for the seven-league boots of the fairytale; they enable man to go down into the sea in ships on more or less lawful occasions, and they have endowed him with the wings that he has always longed for but could not hope to get until he reached Heaven. Books are no longer chained up in treasuries but, manifolded by the magic of ink, are to be bought on the street corner like peanuts. Pictures from the private gallery of prince or plutocrat are multiplied by the same mechanism and scattered throughout the land. We do not have to pay five dollars to hear one song by Galli Curci since we can hear her at home with as many encores as we like. Caruso, though dead, yet speaketh. His voice has been embalmed by carbolic acid. Events that few could witness are brought to us all on the celluloid film. So, whether it be the satisfaction of our material wants or the gratification of our aspiration for art and literature, the chemist acts as the agent of applied democracy.

While we are thus extolling the powers and virtues of chemistry, let us keep in mind that this mastery over nature which the chemist gives to man is a mastery over energy. All wealth—indeed, all matter—is in essence energy. As Slosson points out, the rise and fall of nations is a manifestation of their ability to store, release, and utilize energy. The sources of energy are practically but two, food and fuel, very similar in composition and in their final products. The basic reaction on which our vital and mechanical powers depend is the oxidation of carbon and hydrogen.[6]

Food and fuel—those are the two great necessities of

[6] For the materials of the preceding, and the next paragraph I am indebted to Dr. Slosson's essay on "The Energy of the New World" in the volume, *Society Today*, in the series of volumes on *Man and His World*, D. Van Nostrand Co.

man and society. If the fuel falls short, life itself will be limited. If the food falls short, our modern civilization will disappear, and humanity will revert to a primitive condition. Eventually all our food and fuel, our muscular and machine power, depend upon the peculiar ability of the little green granules of vegetation to build up carbohydrates out of the air and water. The green leaf reaction—the chlorophyll reaction—is the sole support of all plant and vegetable life, and without it the earth would be a desert planet like the moon. As Dr. Slosson says:

If the work of the world were really done by "horse power" as we still call it, man would have reached the limits of civilization a hundred years ago, for a horse requires hay and hay requires land and there would not be enough land in the world to provide for the horse power we are now using. Supplementing the green fields with the coal fields, man has not only prevented civilization from coming to a stop, but has given it an unprecedented impetus. The iron horse feeds on subterranean pastures. He is living on crops of the Carboniferous Era. Modern civilization basks in the sunshine that fell upon the earth unmeasured millennia ago. We are living on our capital, drawing on the coal banks. Sometime we must begin to earn our own living, to grow our fuel as we go.[7]

In the last sentence we have a prediction and a warning. Today we are living upon the carbonaceous capital bequeathed us by the earth ages ago. But some day our inheritance of coal and oil will run out. This would compel a severe change in our mode of living, unless we were prepared for the emergency. There is but one way to avoid this fate, and that is to discover new sources of energy, or devise a better method of capturing solar energy than planets have hit upon. This is the greatest scientific problem a future generation will have to solve.

[7] Quoted from the essay, "The Human Side of Chemistry," *loc. cit.*

And now, in the remaining paragraphs of this chapter, for purposes of clarification and emphasis, we are restating the fundamental thesis.

The present theory may be called an energetic conception of nature, of physical, biological and social evolution. In this respect we are quite in line with Dr. A. N. Whitehead's organic philosophy of nature. Science, Dr. Whitehead [8] says, is the study of organisms; biology is the study of larger organisms; whereas physics is the study of smaller organisms. Whitehead's view that the elements of the physical world consist of the vibratory ebb and flow of an underlying energy or activity (*op. cit.*, p. 53) appears to have been an anticipation of de Broglie's undulatory theory of the electron and seems to be in harmony with Schrödinger's doctrine of wave mechanics.

On the biological level the same energetic interpretation holds. As Dr. Lotka points out,[9] since the fundamental object of contention in the life struggle in the evolution of the organic world is available energy, the advantage must go to those organisms whose energy-capturing devices are the most efficient. In addition to directing energy into channels advantageous to itself, there will also result an increase in the total mass of the organic system which serves as the seat of the energy flux, for this energy flux is proportional to the mass of the system. This view of Dr. Lotka may be summed up in the statement that natural selection will so operate as to increase the total mass of the organic system, to increase the rate of circulation of matter through the system, and to increase to a maximum the total energy flux

---

[8] *Science and the Modern World*, 1926, p. 150.
[9] "Contributions to the Energetics of Evolution," *Proceedings of the National Academy of Science*, 1922, Vol. 8, no. 6.

through the system, so far as compatible with the restraints to which the system is subject.

Other investigators have developed a view similar to that of Dr. Lotka, applied to man as an energy transformer. Dr. Smith Ely Jelliffe,[10] to mention but one, tells us that the human body, like all living matter, is an energy system for the capture, transformation and release of energy. Specific receptors have been evolved for the capture of energy, definite organs have become structuralized to handle the incoming energy and transform it, so that effector organs of varying complexity may discharge it. An organism is thus regarded as an aggregate of structuralized functions or activities. An organ, therefore, is a bit of structuralized experiences of enormous mnemic capacity to handle in a definite and reliable way this interchange of energy-inflow and behavior-outgo.

Continuing this energetic story through its transition into the human social milieu, we note what Dr. Slosson has pointed out, that civilization is based upon the capture, utilization and release of energy. In that respect society resembles an organism. Humanity has progressively conquered the land, the sea, the air through the invention of more efficient machines to transform and use energy. As Dr. Slosson says, the mobility of man is measured by the mobility of the power he employs. And since all work means the using up of free or potential energy, it follows that the further advancement of human progress, or even the maintenance of our present standards of living, depends upon the more efficient utilization of present supplies of energy or the discovery of new sources of energy.

The number of people who can live upon our earth and the comfort in which they live depend upon how

[10] *Archives of Neurology and Psychiatry,* 1924, Vol. 12, 380-410.

much energy can be obtained and how economically it
can be used. Hence from an ethical point of view that
nation which makes the best use of its potential energies
deserves the most credit. We might sum up the ethical
aspect of the problem in what Ostwald called the energetic imperative, which, as applied to individuals, runs
as follows: *So act that the crude energy is transformed
into the higher with the least possible loss.*[11] This formulation is regarded by Ostwald as being more definite
and universal than Kant's categorical imperative; but
from the point of view of ethics the real problem has
just begun, for we still have to determine what criterion
to employ in distinguishing between "low" and "high"
forms of energy. Ostwald's criterion is the relative importance of energies for human purposes. But this seems
quite vague. For example, consider the following statement: "Not only do murder and war destroy cultural
values without substituting others in their place, not
only do the countless conflicts which take place between
different nations and political organizations act anticul-
turally, but so also do the conflicts between the various
social classes of one nation, for they destroy quantities
of free energy which are thus withdrawn from the total
of real cultural values." Is it clear here that war is condemned because it violates the energetic imperative? Is
there not reason to suspect that Ostwald condemns war
because he has another, implicit and unstated, test of
what he regards as "real cultural values"?

[11] Quoted from E. E. Slosson's book, *Major Prophets of Today*, 1916,
chapter on Wilhelm Ostwald, p. 203.

CHAPTER XII

THE PHILOSOPHY OF ENERGETICS

THE term energy, like the notion of force, developed out of human experience. We speak of feeling "energetic" when we are capable of doing work. This popular conception of energy as the ability to do work is in keeping with the scientific definition, except that in physics the "dimensions" of energy are exactly specified, as follows:

$$Energy = force \times distance$$
$$\text{where}$$
$$Force = mass \times acceleration$$

Therefore, speaking technically, the energy a man expends in any interval of time is equal to the rate at which he expends energy (through muscular activity) times the period of time he works. Further proof of this fact that we get our idea of energy from our sense of effort involved in doing muscular work [1] is seen in the

---

[1] It is now fashionable to say that energy, thus defined, is a result of anthropomorphism; it is also stated that science has expunged all elements of anthropomorphism and relics of primitive animism from physics. But in a sense all the concepts of science are anthropomorphic or man-made. I have some sympathy with the view of Schopenhauer, who believes that we have the experience of energy in what we call *will*, and I am also inclined to side with Herbert Spencer when he affirms that in lifting a weight the experience of effort in pulling up must be a clue to the "pull" which nature "exerts" downward. I, for one, am willing to say that the nerve current which the biochemist records as an electro-chemical change is experienced subjectively as an "act of will." This, however, does not commit us to the old doctrine of the "freedom of the will."

For a further statement of this view see the writer's paper, "Evolu-

fact that the notion of kinetic energy comes from the belief in *vis viva,* or living force as a property of moving matter.[2] According to Professor R. A. Millikan,[3] "the word energy as a precise physical concept was not in the English dictionary until 1850. When Helmholtz wrote his remarkable essay in 1847—and this was one of the essays that set the principle of the conservation of energy going—in the title of this essay he confused two ideas, those of force and energy, which we would not allow a sophomore in the high school to confuse today."

In the broadest sense of the term, there are only two forms of energy, *potential* energy and *kinetic* energy. When work is done energy is converted from this first to the second form. Thus when a man lifts a heavy stone, the potential energy stored up in the muscles is converted into the kinetic energy of the contraction of the muscles of the arms and back, etc. In all cases, however, the human being must eventually rely upon the potential energy stored up in the food he eats, as this is converted into available energy through the digestive processes in order to be burned up by the body through oxidation.

Potential energy can exist in various forms. There are electric, chemical, mechanical, and other forms of energy available for doing work. While the initiation of any kind of activity results from taking potential energy of some form and converting it into kinetic energy of motion, the transformations of energies (*e.g.,* from thermal

tion, Consciousness, and Electricity," *Psyche,* July, 1931, and the article, "Energy the Soul of Matter," *Journal of Religion,* 1932, Vol. 12, 61-79.

[2] The history of the notion of energy is summarized by the writer in an article, "A Spiritual Behaviorism," *The Monist,* 1927, Vol. 37, 289-308.

[3] Phi Beta Kappa Address, published in the *New York Times,* Dec. 21, 1930.

to mechanical) take place in accordance with certain uniform laws of physics. These principles are usually termed the laws of thermodynamics (or energetics), of which there are two: the law of the conservation of energy and the law of the degradation of energy.

The first law of energetics, the law of the conservation of energy, was established through the work of Davy, Rumford, Joule, and others in the earlier part of the nineteenth century. Professor Millikan [4] states that the principle of the conservation of energy is probably the most far-reaching physical principle ever developed. The law is commonly understood to mean that while energy can be transformed—electric energy into heat energy, heat energy into mechanical energy, etc.—there is always a constant ratio of transformation and one can never get more out of the new form than there was available in the old form. Frequently the amount of energy gotten out for useful work is less, and this would be illustrated by the conversion of the potential energy of coal into the kinetic energy of the molecules of steam in a boiler which, by their expansive pressure, move the piston of the steam engine. Here there is a loss of energy for useful work, though no energy is destroyed or lost. The principle of the conservation of energy decrees that you cannot get something for nothing; a perpetual motion machine is therefore impossible if by such a machine one means an engine that can give out more energy than it takes in.

As we shall see in discussing the second law of energetics, it is not ordinarily possible to get as much energy out of a machine in work done as is put into the engine, for the most perfect machine possible (one which em-

[4] "Present Status of Theory and Experiment as to Atomic Disintegration and Atomic Synthesis," *Science*, 1931, Vol. 73, p. 1.

ployed almost perfectly frictionless bearings) cannot completely escape the price levied by nature in the form of a loss of some otherwise available energy through heat radiation.

An alternative way of stating this law that energy can neither be created nor destroyed is found in the generalization that the sum-total of energy in the universe is constant. That is,

$$E_p + E_k = K \text{ (a constant)}$$

A few years back this law was regarded as being so firmly established that nothing could overthrow it. Along with the doctrine of Lavoisier that matter can neither be created nor destroyed, the principle of the conservation of energy was taken as providing one of the foundation stones of physical science. In recent years this attitude has undergone a modification. The "law" may be attacked from two sides, the theoretical and the experimental. It is now argued by some that the first law of energetics is really a kind of mental postulate or convention. We suppose that something in this universe must be constant (on the old Greek theory that out of nothing nothing can come), and we call this something "energy." If, in any given case, energy does appear to vanish into non-existence, we refuse to believe what appears to be the fact, and proceed to invent a new kind of potential energy to balance the accounts, as Poincaré has pointed out. Thus, it is said, the law is analogous to the famous law of mathematics that there are three feet to the yard—both are true by proclamation!

The more empirical attack on this law of the conservation of energy begins with experiments indicating that matter is a form of energy and can be converted into energy. This in itself does not upset the law, for the increase of radiant or electromagnetic energy does not mean the *de novo* creation of energy. If the sun's energy, which is being radiated continuously out into space, comes from the destruction of tons of mass of matter—a doctrine entirely consistent with Einstein's theory of relativity, which holds that matter is a form of energy—this involves no increase in the sum-total of energy in the universe. But the fact that the one process occurs suggests that the reverse process of the conversion of energy back into matter (atoms) may also occur, and if this be the case, the principle of the conservation of energy must be modified in some way. If on the average as much energy is being converted into matter as matter is being converted into energy, then the first law of energetics is true in a statistical way. The new law of conservation might be put as follows: the sum-total of matter-energy in the universe is constant. If, however, the relation is not reversible, but goes only one way, from matter to energy, then the universe must come to an end in the ultimate dissolution of matter. This is the view favored by Sir J. H. Jeans and A. S. Eddington; whereas R. A. Millikan holds to the view that matter is actually being created out in the depths of space, and so he does not look for the ultimate extinction of the physical universe.

These developments leave physics in a state which is baffling to the layman and the expert alike. But in spite of all uncertainties the conclusion seems to be emerging that energy is the fundamental and abiding reality of the universe. This is the modern scientific version of Huxley's statement that nothing endures in the universe save the ordered flow of energy.

With reference to the philosophical significance of the principle of the conservation of energy, it may be stated that in general an exclusive emphasis upon this law has thrown scientific philosophy in the direction of materialism. By basing his philosophy on the first law of energetics Ernst Haeckel was brought around to the materialistic view stated in his famous work, *The Riddle of the Universe*. The strong presumption (based on experiment) that this principle applies to the energy transformations resident in living matter, no less than to inorganic systems, has constituted an outstanding objection to the doctrine that men had minds (or souls) the decisions of which were imposed upon the body, for this appeared to violate the first law of energetics. More recently some psychological dualists have seized upon the fact that the principle is now under criticism in physics as justification for putting it aside as an objection to the supposed interaction of soul and body; but we must not forget that no one has yet shown that the human body has any other source of energy for its responses than through the energy taken in by way of the foods we eat, with their various calorie contents.

And now we come to the discussion of the meaning of the second law of thermodynamics.

Unlike the principle of the conservation of energy, the second law is not the result of any intellectual assumption which is superimposed upon nature. It describes our actual apprehensions of nature's processes. In its most general form the principle tells us what we all know: that water runs down hill; that fried eggs cannot be unscrambled; that a cigaret once smoked can never be called back into existence in its original form. In a more exact form this principle is a recognition of the empirical fact that while *e.g.*, electrical energy can be completely converted into heat, the reverse process of the conversion of heat into other forms of energy cannot be completely accomplished. Thus this principle really appears to mean that certain types of processes in nature are irreversible. Whenever in any process there is a conversion of energy into heat, this is radiated off into space, and is then lost so far as its availability for doing more work is concerned.

As stated earlier, the second law of thermodynamics is sometimes called the principle of the degradation of energy. Dr. Slosson sums this up in the statement that nature is the complete communist, the universal leveler, for if nature had her way, all mountains would be worn flat, all rivers received into the sea, all temperatures reduced to their lowest common denominator (heat), all energy dissipated and diffused. Physics presents the picture of a universe running down to an ultimate heat-death (*wärmetod*). Physics tells us that the cosmic clock must eventually come to a stop, unless, as Millikan avers, there is some self-winding mechanism (like Maxwell's famous sorting demons) at work somewhere, or somebody outside the entire contrivance (as J. H. Jeans supposes) who can wind it up when occasion demands. It is interesting to note in passing that at this point Dr. Jeans's conception of God is reminiscent of the God of traditional Calvinistic theology.

The second law is an empirical law in the sense that it is based on experience. We know of no essential reason why things should work that way. Perhaps in the world beyond the reaches of our present senses nature does turn back upon herself. But within the limits of human experience this fact of irreversibility may be generalized in several ways. For the physicist the most satisfactory way to generalize the fact is to say that all things happen in such a way that a certain mathematical function, called *entropy*, tends to increase. That is to say, the law which states that energy tends to be degraded, that the potential (free) energy tends to decrease or be used up, is summarized mathematically in the statement that the entropy of the universe tends towards a maximum. Since, as Boltzmann put it, entropy is proportional to the logarithm of the probability of a certain state, we must conclude that nature passes from less probable to more probable states.

The question has been raised as to whether living systems obey this same principle. The vitalists argue that the phenomena of living organisms are not deducible from the laws of energetics. Helmholtz was the first to suggest that organisms might not obey the second law. Since then, Hans Driesch has suggested that *entelechy* (the term which Driesch takes over from Aristotle as a name for the Vital force) might suspend the operation of this law, and Henri Bergson has also supposed that *l'elan vital* may retard the tendency towards the degradation of energy. This is the position of those who hold that life is some unique or non-physical agent of some sort.[5]

On the other hand the gestalt psychologists attempt to explain such an obviously purposive response as the visual fixation reaction in terms of this law, as we have previously indicated. It has even been supposed that Pavlov's laws of the conditioned reflex can be derived from the second law of thermodynamics applied to biochemical processes. With such illustrations before us, it is clear that we should be cautious in stating categorically that organisms can violate this very general principle of physical chemistry.[6]

[5] For a more detailed statement of this idea see James Johnstone's, *The Mechanism of Life*, London, 1921.

[6] A brief discussion of this problem is presented by Sir W. M. Bayliss in his address, *Life and the Laws of Thermodynamics*, Oxford University Press, 1922.

In this case, as in all similar situations, the question of the applicability of the laws of energetics to living organisms must be decided by experiment, but supposing that these laws are, and always can be, shown to hold, is it not clear by now that this does not commit us to a "mechanistic" view? It seems so to me. We have constantly insisted upon the idea that the irreversibility of human conscious experience must have some chemical counterpart in the human body, and the only biochemical process which can provide the irreversible underpinning for the unidirectionality of experienced time is the second law of thermodynamics.

It must be pointed out that the second law of thermodynamics is neither "mechanical" nor "supermechanical." The writer [7] has pointed out in detail that there is a duality of natural law, as follows: (a) causal laws (illustrated by the principle of *least action,* which includes the law of the conservation of energy as a special case), giving determinism and predictability, and (b) *statistical laws,* yielding mere probability and introducing indeterminism into our calculations. The real distinction between these two types of laws lies in the point of view each represents. In the case of dynamical laws we can visualize the entities concerned and follow their activities in detail, but in statistical laws we deal with aggregates and mean values. Furthermore, dynamical (or causal) laws are reversible, while statistical laws express irreversibility. This dualism, associated with the distinction between the reversible and the irreversible, is an expression of the "atomistic" and the "phenomenological" points of view. We have already noted that A. S. Eddington [8] favors such a dualism of laws as we have outlined,

[7] "Probability, Natural Law, and Emergence," *Journal of Philosophy,* 1926, Vol. 23, 421-434. See also the Introduction to the present volume.
[8] *The Nature of the Physical World,* p. 75.

which he expresses by the distinction between what he calls *primary* and *secondary* laws. The contrasts which Eddington enumerates parallel in several respects those which the writer has noted. According to Eddington, a primary law holds for the behavior of individuals and is indifferent to time direction; whereas a secondary law holds for aggregates rather than individuals, expresses probable rather than necessary results, and therefore introduces "chance" into our dealing with nature. The second law of thermodynamics, illustrating a secondary law, gives to time the arrow which indicates direction and irreversibility.

According to the present view, statistical laws are interpreted in a phenomenal sense. By this we mean that in such cases we are studying ensembles which *exhibit* or *express* themselves. The second law of thermodynamics is interpreted to mean that the entities concerned have come to some common basis of functional pattern (or *gestalt*). The tendency of "matter" to lose energy to the ether is but an expression of the tendency for particles to enter into dynamic intercourse with their environments, to produce a macroscopic state. One illustration of such a macroscopic pattern is seen in botany. Like the biochemist, who studies the intimate and complex mechanisms of plants, we may analyze the petals of flowers into their intricate molecular structures. But we may also view the flower from the "descriptive" point of view, as a phenomenal pattern. This is the attitude of appreciation. We all know that the flower, in spite of its detailed complexity, possesses an emergent simplicity, which is responsible for its beauty to us. For us the notion of entropy is the thermodynamic correlate of the energic streaming (objective in the flower and subjective in us in the experience of beauty) whereby the pattern expresses itself.

This means, then, that it is the second law of thermodynamics which underlies the emergence of macroscopic (or phenomenal) patterns (or gestalten) out of statistical ensembles of microscopic elements. This interpretation is not explicitly stated in Eddington's exposition. And yet what we have here set forth is consistent with his view. Professor Eddington tells us (*op. cit.* pp. xiv-xv) that the external world has become a *shadow world*, and that the drama of familiar life, from the point of view of present day physics, is a shadowgraph performance. And now we ask, why should we not identify this "moving row of magic shadow shapes that come and go" with the phenomenological world which "expresses" itself? And why should not the second law of thermodynamics be taken as providing the physical basis for these macroscopic patterns, these emergent gestalten? Eddington almost comes upon this view when he tells us (p. 105) that *entropy* is to be placed along side *beauty* and *melody* (both of them gestalten, since they are non-summative wholes), because it meets the essential requirement that all three appear as features of *arrangement*. That nature does in fact produce new (or emergent) simplicities out of complexities of parts through the averaging process inherent in statistical ensembles is the contention of Dr. G. N. Lewis [9] in the following lines:

The interaction between two bodies is treated by the methods of mechanics; the interaction of a billion such bodies must be treated by the statistical methods of thermodynamics. These are the same bodies and presumably follow the same behavior, but a great group of new phenomena *emerges* when

[9] *The Anatomy of Science*, p. 184.

we study an immense number, and by this we mean merely that phenomena appear that never would have been recognized or dreamed of if the two bodies alone had been studied.

However, to me it seems clear that whenever there is *interaction* between the members of a statistical aggregate, these constituent elements are no longer the "same" bodies, as Professor Lewis asserts them to be, for the properties of the parts are now determined in part by the properties of the new whole.

In our own view the second law of energetics is so generalized as to refer to "social" situations, whether on the molecular or the human level. The individuals which enter into the production of a social order are relative. From the point of view of the kinetic theory of gases, the molecules of a gas are unitary entities, though from the viewpoint of a lower level they may be very complex. And so it is with human beings. In its statistical investigations sociology deals with human beings as unitary individuals, but the human being, from a biological point of view, is a very complex system of systems. Elsewhere [10] the writer has suggested that the permanence of substance arises from the fact that when a group of random movements (*e.g.*, of molecules) is organized into a new "stuff" (*e.g.*, a body of water, or a stone) the unity of the new aggregate expresses the central tendency of a statistical configuration of elements. A thing expresses the range of behavior of elements varying about a mean position, and therefore represents a kind of statistical constancy of high stability. This allows us to regard the human self as a kind of average of the various psychic "isotopes" which make up that miniature social system of which each of us is constituted. Thus whether the

[10] "Matter and the Present Outlook of Science," *Scientia*, July, 1928, and "Physics and the Laws of Thought," *Psyche*, April, 1931.

human individual is "simple" or "complex" depends on the purpose and the level of our analysis.

The same reasoning applies to the social group as a collection of selves. That is to say, the interaction between human individuals to produce a society illustrates on a higher level our interpretation of the second law of thermodynamics. It is interesting to note that the present view is similar to that of Ostwald (though developed independently) and finds some confirmation in the following lines quoted at length from Ostwald [11]:

It is a strange thing indeed that by merely being associated with another thing of the same kind identity is lost. And still more strange is the fact that every being of this kind seems driven by an irresistible impulse to seek every occasion for losing its identity. Every known physical fact leads to the conclusion that diffusion, or a homogeneous distribution, of energy is the general aim of all happenings. No change whatever seems to have occurred, and probably none ever will occur, resulting in a concentration greater than the corresponding dissipation of energy. A partial concentration may be brought about in a system, but only at the expense of a greater dissipation, and the sum total is always an increase in dissipation.

While we are as sure as science can make us about the general validity of this law as applied to the physical world, its application to human development may be doubted. It seems to me to hold good in this case also, if it is applied with proper caution. The difficulty lies in the circumstance that we have no exact objective means of measuring homogeneity and heterogeneity in human affairs, and we can therefore not study any given system closely enough to draw a quantitative conclusion. It seems pretty certain that increase of culture tends to diminish the differences between men. It equalizes not only the general standard of living, but attenuates also even the natural differences of sex and age. From this point of view I should look upon the accumulation of

[11] Quoted from E. E. Slosson's *Major Prophets of Today*, pp. 227-8.

enormous wealth in the hands of a single man as indicating an imperfect state of culture.

The property which has been described as an irresistible tendency toward diffusion may also be observed in certain cases in man. In conscious beings such natural tendencies are accompanied by a certain feeling which we call will, and we are happy when we are allowed to act according to these tendencies or according to our will. Now, if we recall the happiest moments of our lives, they will be found in every case to be connected with this curious loss of personality. In the happiness of love this fact will be at once discovered. . . .

One might point out in passing that this psychological fact was clearly recognized by Jesus in such statements as these: "Whosoever would become great among you shall be your minister, and whosoever would be first among you shall be your servant, even as the Son of man came not to be ministered unto, but to minister" (*Matt.* xx, 26-28); and "He that seeketh his life shall lose it, and he that loseth his life for my sake and the Gospels shall find it." It was Nietzsche's psychic blindness to the spiritual significance of the second law of thermodynamics which was responsible for his distorted conception of the Superman.

It has sometimes been argued that the statistical regularity of human conduct proves that human behavior is "mechanical" in the same way in which the behavior of the molecules of a gas is mechanical. The fact that the number of marriages, births (legitimate and illegitimate), suicides, etc., remains fairly constant from year to year, or decreases and increases uniformly with the variation of certain environmental conditions (or parameters) such as relative "good" times and "bad" times, is taken to mean that human conduct is subject to laws of a mechanistic sort, so that human purposes do not count. But from our point of view this entire argument loses its significance. It is not at all clear just what is meant by a "mechanistic" explanation, but surely the actual regularity in the behavior of human beings in society does not prove that the behavior of individuals is not purposive. It may only prove that there is a statistical constancy in the nature of the purposes which all human beings have.

It may be stated as a general rule that no necessary conclusion is suggested by statistical laws concerning the nature of the "mechanisms" that are supposed to determine the behavior of the individual events making up the statistical ensemble under consideration. Thermodynamics possesses the advantages of a statistical approach, but it also suffers from what some would regard as a defect in failing to reveal the intimate nature of the interactions of the elements. Representing as it does a purely phenomenalistic or descriptive approach, the second law of thermodynamics is free from any necessary "mechanistic" implications. Thus thermodynamics has the strength of its weakness.

CHAPTER XIII

THE EMERGENCE OF CULTURAL PATTERNS

I. Emergent Evolution

EVERYONE is familiar with the phenomenon in the physical world known as *inertia*. In general this is the tendency of a thing to continue to do what it has been doing, so that if the thing has been at rest it requires some time (brief or long, depending on the mass of the body and the amount of the force applied to it) to set it in motion, or if it has been in motion it requires time and the application of an opposing force to bring it to rest. This law, universal in its application in physical nature, has also been shown to hold in physiological processes. We know, for example, that it requires time and energy to set a sense organ, such as the eye, into activity. And after the retina has been excited, the activity tends to continue for a brief interval of time after the cessation of the physical stimulus. This phenomenon is referred to as the *time lag* of a process.

It would not be at all strange if this law also held in the intellectual and cultural spheres. And our expectations are here fulfilled, for it is known that in social processes there is a "cultural lag" analogous to the time lag in physical and physiological processes. The human mind certainly exhibits inertia, for if you want to set the mind of man in action you must apply sufficient energy to overcome intellectual resistance. It is for this reason that the application in society of theoretical ideas and inventions discovered by research workers does not bear practical fruits in society until some time after their inception. In this sense popular beliefs, codes of ethics, and practical applications are invariably behind the times, frequently so much as a generation, a century, or even longer. But while the public live by one set of beliefs and practises, research workers are laboring in their sanctuaries to create new patterns of theory and practise, destined eventually to replace old and outworn patterns. And this process of creating new fashions, applying them in practise, subsequently to discard them because obsolete, continues and will continue so long as civilization endures.

In matters of styles it is always hazardous to attempt to anticipate the future. But signs and portents indicate that a new set of intellectual fashions is in process of creation, and the temptation is irresistible to infer coming events from shadows cast before. As yet these fashions are in the experimental stage, being cut and trimmed as one might say, in the private workshops of the experts. In time they will be ready for a public fitting, and then we shall know whether they really constitute the new styles for the intelligent layman of the future. The new modes we have in mind are now known to the experts as the theory of "emergent evolution" and the doctrine of "gestalt psychology," two views we have already referred to on occasion. These doctrines have much in common, and, if true, possess important implications for science, philosophy and religion. Some of the general outlines of these theories are now taking form; if the reader will accompany us, we will do a bit of peeping to see what we can discover behind the screen. But let us first go back a bit in the history of thought.

The history of thought is to a considerable extent the record of the successive attempts on the part of investigators to find the answers to certain recurring questions. These problems have as persistently stimulated the minds of thinkers as they have baffled their ingenuity. The problems here referred to have to do with certain *dualisms* which have been established, then to be passed on from age to age as a kind of cultural heritage. Generally speaking, a dualism results when we have two kinds of entities or types of processes which are supposed to interact in some manner still to be explained. The two end-terms of the dualism may come into existence in several different ways. We may *create them intellectually* (*i.e.*, by postulation), or we may *discover them empirically* (*i.e.*, find them by actual observation of some domain of nature). Of course, a combination of the two methods is also possible. In the first case our problem is not a genuine one for science: in natural science a problem which has only subjective significance is a "pseudo-problem." It is only in the second case that we have a real scientific problem, in the sense that nature then presents to us two kinds of realities or processes which are different in kind, while yet interacting causally in some manner to be discovered and explained.

The history of human thought presents us with a number of such dualisms, several of which we have referred to in previous chapters. As is well known, from primitive thought and Greek philosophy modern thought has inherited the dualism of *soul* and *body*. In modern psychological theory this dualism still persists, though in a diluted form, in the distinction between a conscious process and a nervous process. Another such dichotomy appears in biology in the distinction between a living principle, the vital force, and protoplasm, the "physical basis of life." Even physics has not entirely escaped this mode of thinking, for the older dualism of *force* and *matter* seems to reflect the type of explanation illustrated by the above dualisms in biology and psychology.

A little reflection will make it clear that the sharper one draws the line of demarcation between the two end-terms of any dualism the more difficult becomes the problem of explaining the interaction between the realities concerned. Taking the case, for example, of the dualism of soul and body, we find that at the beginning of modern thought the French philosopher and mathematician, René Descartes, defined the soul as unextended thinking substance and matter as extended and unthinking substance. Matter is spatial and the soul non-spatial, according to Descartes. In framing these definitions Descartes virtually created the modern problem of explaining how the unextended soul could act on the extended body, when the two have nothing in common. Such supposed interaction seems to violate the common principle that the cause and the effect must resemble each other (*i.e.*, if the effect is physical the cause is physical), not to mention the alleged violation of the principle of the conservation of energy previously discussed.

In stating the distinction in this way Descartes really presented modern philosophy with an insoluble problem. All the theorists who have accepted this distinction have failed at showing how this assumed interaction between soul and body could occur. In the end investigators have been forced to admit that the *modus operandi* of such interaction is not understood.

Other theorists have attempted to deal with the problem of the explanation of human behavior in other ways. The "materialist" disposes of the dualism by reducing everything in the universe to terms of one fundamental reality, material substance. The "soul" becomes a name for certain bodily functions not yet completely understood. In the words of Thomas Hobbes, thinking is but the motion of some peculiar substance in the head. The modern behaviorist improves upon this by transferring the motion which is thought from the head to the muscles, especially the larynx, so that thinking becomes "subvocal speech." Unfortunately for the behaviorist, the physical theory on which materialism has been based is now definitely exploded. Whatever matter may be, it certainly is not what the materialists, ancient or modern, have declared it to be. Another school of thinkers, the idealists, sensing the difficulties of materialism, have attempted to abolish the dualism of the physical and the psychical by reducing everything to terms of one fundamental spiritual reality. Idealism is materialism inverted. Berkeley made the most sustained effort to work out the details of such a conception. But in spite of the Bishop's cleverness, no one today believes this theory—unless it be the Christian Scientists.

In consequence of this historical development, modern speculative thought found itself in a blind alley. Philosophy degenerated into the give and take of refutations and counter-refutations. There was lacking any freshness of vision without which philosophy becomes stale, flat and unprofitable. In such a situation what is to be done? The answer to this question has been given by Professor W. M. Wheeler,[1] who tells us that "when thinking tends to congeal into two conflicting interpretations we naturally either devote our days to showing why the one must be true and the other false, or we seek to escape both by adopting a new position." This is what the

[1] See his book, *Emergent Evolution and the Development of Societies.*

"emergent evolutionists" attempt to do—escape from the materialism-idealism dilemma by adopting a new position. And thus a new breath of life sweeps through the otherwise stale corridors of modern philosophy.

The advocates of this view feel that at last we have an interpretation which tells us the truth about nature and her processes. In this new compromise ancient antitheses are wiped out. We are told, in the words of Professor Wheeler, that "with the extension of the concepts of emergence and organicism also to the physical, chemical, psychological and social domains, there arises the strong probability that the old 'nothing but' attitudes of naturalism *versus* supernaturalism, materialism *versus* spiritualism, mechanism *versus* vitalism, determinism *versus* freedom, and pluralism *versus* monism, etc., may be abandoned and the way opened up for a more consistent and more satisfying view of universal reality."

Here we have summed up in concise form what is held to be the most significant claim made for the doctrine of emergent evolution: it professes to show us the way to avoid the necessity of making a choice between extreme views. There is another possibility, not provided for in the previous alternatives.

We see that the promises held out by this doctrine are indeed attractive. It is not surprising, therefore, to find prominent thinkers, scientists and philosophers alike, embracing this view. To be sure, the doctrine does not mean the same thing to all its advocates. But before touching upon the matter of individual differences of interpretation, let us get the more general outlines of the theory before us.

The term *emergent evolution* is a name for the process whereby *new* effects (or processes) arise from the operation of antecedent causes (or processes). In the course of the historical order new wholes (or configurations) appear (emerge) which contain or exhibit *novel* properties, properties different from the result of a summation of the properties of the constituent parts. In brief, empirical nature does not always respect human arithmetic: two plus two does not always equal four.

At this point it is necessary to make a distinction between *emergent effects* and *resultant effects*. In physics, the reader will recall, the term "resultant" is used in connection with the "parallelogram of forces." Consider by way of example a body acted upon by two forces (vectors) operating at right angles to each other with the same amount of force. In this case the path of the body is represented by the resultant, the diagonal formed when the parallelogram (in this case a square) is completed. Here the direction and amount of the effect can be predicted in advance; in general such a resultant effect represents the summation or addition (either algebraic or geometric) of the parts. But there is another type of process in which the effects are not summative. In such cases the parts interact dynamically to produce a whole in which the parts are no longer independent of each other. Here we are dealing with an emergent effect. In a human being, for example, the "unity of personality" is something other than the sum of the various reflexes and habits into which our behavior may be analyzed. The situation here is quite different from the arrangement of the pieces of furniture in a room, where individual parts may be added to or taken away without disturbing the remainder. In an emergent whole (the *gestalt* of gestalt psychology) the entire configuration acts as a unit, made up of parts to be sure; but such phenomena as are illustrated by the behavior of water —with its "wetness," surface tension, ability to quench thirst, put out fires, etc.—cannot be deduced from a knowledge of the properties of the individual constituents.

In order to clarify the thesis of the emergent evolutionists let us contrast this view with the picture of nature outlined by Laplace. As is generally known, Laplace made the claim that from a knowledge of the number, distribution, and law of interaction of the ultimate particles in the universe an *infinite calculator* could predict the entire future of the universe. A similar claim was made by John Tyndall when he supposed that the plays of Shakespeare were somehow wrapped up in the primitive fire-mist from which Laplace supposed our own solar system to have evolved. Now an emergent evolutionist would flatly deny this contention. He might attack the doctrine in several ways. For one thing, he might point out, the mechanist is guilty of a dialectical subterfuge. When the mechanist states that if we knew all the causes, all the facts in any case, we could predict the properties and the behavior of any system, or any system of systems, such as nature as a whole, he defines "all" in such a way as to be synonymous with the ability to predict completely, so that in cases where such prediction is impossible the mechanist can assert that this is so because we don't know all. This tautology appears in Laplace's infinite calculator; he can predict the entire future of the course of nature because he is *defined* to be a creature with that superhuman ability.

In the second place, the emergent evolutionist might point out, many physicists today are apparently less favorably disposed toward the classical mechanical theory which Laplace assumed when he made the claim. On the classical theory, in order to predict one had to know the position and velocity of each particle in the

universe at some given instant. But we are now told
that we cannot ascribe both to the same particle at
the same time, at least when we are dealing with electrons. If we state the velocity of an electron we cannot
state its position, and if we state its position we cannot
state its velocity. But both are necessary if Laplace's
claim is to be validated. This idea has been emphasized
by Eddington when he quotes a statement ascribed to
Heisenberg, as follows: "The question of whether, from
a complete knowledge of the past one could predict the
future does not arise, because a complete knowledge of
the past is impossible" (*op. cit.*, p. 228).

Some philosophers have made this same point in another way. The phrase, the "infinite regress of causes,"
refers to the fact that in any causal analysis the particular cause which we assign to a given effect is itself the
effect of other causes, so that theoretically we can push
back our analysis as far as we please, without reaching a
"first cause." This means that to understand any single
event fully one would have to understand the entire universe, past and present (perhaps also the future), and
this is obviously impossible.

Of course, as various persons have pointed out, even
though we admit that we cannot assign a position and a
velocity to a particle, this does not mean necessarily
that particles do not have both at the same time. It is
pointed out that the very fact that when dealing with
a very large number of particles a certain statistical
regularity is observed by nature must mean an underlying determinism in the elements of the statistical aggregate. But even in such cases, as we have previously
noted, new properties may appear in the macroscopic
whole which are not apparent in the microscopic constituents. Thus the notion of "temperature" cannot be

gotten out of the concept of molecules, defined in terms of structure (mass, shape, radius, etc.).[2] It is meaningless to attach the notion of "heat" to individual molecules. Temperature is a statistical notion; the temperature of a gas is the result of an averaging effect of a large number of molecular collisions. Like the term "democracy," it is a name for a mode of functioning. In both cases the meaning of the term resides in the dynamic interaction of the individuals of a "society."

What emerges in all cases is a unitary mode of behavior. As I see it, the main value of the doctrine of emergent evolution is that it places a greater emphasis upon the notion of *behavior* and a lesser emphasis upon the notion of *substance* (matter) than traditional theories permitted. On the emergent theory any "entity"—living or non-living—is simply a functional synthesis. A thing, such as a molecule or an organism, is a behavior unit. It may be treated as a "substance" relative to something else into which it may enter as a constituent unit, but it has its own rhythm of behavior. A molecule has the same sort of unity which a whirl-pool or a smoke ring possesses, except that the unity of the latter things is less permanent and more easily disrupted. Even the ultimate constituents are behavior units, according to the latest theories. In the undulatory theory of the electron matter is considered to be a wave-phenomenon. To be sure, there are some phases of Schrödinger's wave mechanics which will probably be altered in the future, but old fashioned materialism is outlawed in all modern physics.

In the same way, *life* and *mind* must be interpreted as names for characteristic modes of *behavior-stuffs* of

[2] On this point see the writer's paper, "Light, Wave Mechanics, and Consciousness," *Journal of Philosophy*, 1928, Vol. 25, 309-317.

different degrees of complexity. Man does not possess a
soul, in the older sense; he *is* a soul, if you wish, in the
sense that he is normally a functional unity (dynamic
synthesis) of integrated levels of behavior. These unified responses represent something new in nature; man's
conduct cannot be deduced from the tropisms of lower
animals. We are *free* in the sense that the laws of behavior of human individuals are different from the laws
of behavior of the chemical elements out of which they
are made.

This is a brief statement of the thesis of emergent
evolution. And now for a few words concerning the origin
and evolution of the idea.

History has repeatedly demonstrated that new ideas
do not spring up in a vacuum. Even though one be an
emergent evolutionist, it must be admitted that there
are always conditioning processes which provide the
mother solution within which the new (emergent) idea
may crystallize. In the present case this fact is again illustrated. The idea of emergent evolution cannot be
regarded as the unique contribution of modern thinkers.
There have been anticipations of the idea in earlier
thought. Just how old the idea will be held to be will
depend upon one's tendencies towards ancestor worship.
The tendency to look to the Greeks for the idea is to be
discouraged, since such an attitude may lead to an obfus-
cation of the meaning of the term. To be sure, Aristotle's
doctrine of *forms* is somewhat similar to the notion of
a *gestalt,* and Plato does tell us in the *Theatetus* that
the meaning of a sentence is something more than the
sum of the meanings of the separate words which make
up the sentence. But if we begin to call the Greek philosophers emergent evolutionists, the term "emergence"

will inevitably lose what little specificity of meaning it now possesses.

If we look for the origins of the idea in modern thought, we find that among English thinkers John Stuart Mill dealt with the notion of emergence in his *Logic,* in his discussion of "heteropathic laws" of causation. George Henry Lewes was the first to use the term "emergent." In his poem, *Abt Volger,* Robert Browning gave poetic form to the idea in his familiar lines about "chordiness" in music:

> *And I know not if, save in this, such gift be*
> *allowed to man*
> *That out of three sounds he frame, not a fourth*
> *sound, but a star.*

Among the Germans Wilhelm Wundt, the reputed founder of experimental psychology, emphasized the same fact in his principle of "creative synthesis"; while von Ehrenfels provided the criteria for the concept of the "form-quality" as employed by gestalt psychology. Among the French, Henri Bergson has sponsored the idea that evolution is creative; but since he regards vitalism as the explanation of this process, he cannot be regarded as an emergent evolutionist.

In America, prior to its recent popularity, this doctrine was advocated by the sociologist Lester F. Ward. Among philosophers, E. G. Spaulding and R. W. Sellars were first in the field cultivating the idea. Professor Spaulding [3] asserts that "The properties of the whole are, at least some of them, new, and in just that respect are a 'law unto themselves' and in that sense free. This does not mean that they are lawless, but only that their

[3] *The New Rationalism,* 1918, Ch. 43.

specific principles of 'behavior' are not identical with those of the parts." It is this idea of the autonomy of each level which is taken as the justification for the statement made by the biologist, H. S. Jennings, that "the doctrine of emergent evolution is the Declaration of Independence for biological science."

The doctrine of emergent evolution first came into prominence when the British philosopher, S. Alexander, erected an imposing metaphysical structure upon the basis of the doctrine of emergence. In his monumental work, *Space, Time and Deity,* Professor Alexander attempted to accomplish what a number of writers had declared to be impossible in the modern world—a comprehensive system of philosophy. The view of Lloyd Morgan, presented in his Gifford Lectures in 1922, appeared after Alexander had presented his version of the doctrine, and contains some divergences, which we cannot here consider.[4]

Let us now consider briefly the views of Dr. A. N. Whitehead, the British mathematician and philosopher, who is now teaching at Harvard University.

As one would expect, Professor Whitehead shows more competence in dealing with the physical aspects of nature than any other emergent evolutionist. It is unfortunate that this physical background cannot be dealt with here. Now it can only be pointed out that Dr. Whitehead is much impressed with what he calls the "creative advance of nature," in which process, pervading the whole of physical nature, things (or rather "events") come into existence that never existed before. For Whitehead the world is *process*—a striving, an ap-

---

[4] For a statement of Lloyd Morgan's conception of the process see his book, *Emergent Evolution,* where he points out the differences between his own interpretation and those of Alexander (in *Space, Time and Deity*) and R. W. Sellars (in *Evolutionary Naturalism*).

petition towards further creativity. The temporal world is passage into novelty; it is incomplete; through its concretions into actuality the cosmos strives for further completeness.[5]

At some points Dr. Whitehead's ideas are strikingly reminiscent of Aristotle; for both reality is the process whereby the potential, the infinite realm of latent possibilities, emerges into actuality. Thus the actual acquires its definiteness through the transmutation of the indeterminate into determinate actuality.

Nature, therefore, is constituted of *actualities* and *potentialities*. These two poles of nature give us the homologue for the relation of the *physical* and the *mental*. The physical pole is that by which the actual deals with what is factual, while the mental pole is that by which the actual deals with the potential, the realm of possibilities. Nature, in brief, is a purposive process moving onward toward achievement. God is the principle in virtue of which the universe is what it is, as compared with what it might be. God is the principle of concretion; He enters into every creative phase of the process, and yet is above change, as the realm of potential forms.

This is a sketchy outline of one of the most profound and intricate systems of metaphysics the world has seen. Considering the doctrine of emergent evolution as a whole, and ignoring minor differences of detail, let us sum up briefly the possible significance of the movement.

It is clear that on the side of theory there is no question of the importance of these views. The rise of the doctrine of emergent evolution and the present interest

[5] Professor Whitehead's most detailed and comprehensive exposition of his views appears in his more recent book, *Process and Reality* (1929). The most readable account of his philosophy is presented in his book, *Science and the Modern World*.

in gestalt psychology are illustrations of the change of attitude among scientists; they are symptoms of revolt against dreary materialisms and the arid mechanistic theories which have managed to live on into the era of modern philosophy. Now all of these are going by the board.

Eventually, of course, as stated at the beginning of this chapter, this change in outlook will reflect itself in a change in popular beliefs and practises. Perhaps for the present-day layman the foregoing interpretation contains little that will give consolation. For a person holding to traditional religious convictions, a doctrine which makes no provision for personal immortality contains little emotional appeal. It is also evident that Dr. Whitehead's abstractly metaphysical conception of God does not lend itself to the purpose of orthodox theology. But few of us who are familiar with the actual evolution of religion expect the conventional religious temper and viewpoint to endure indefinitely, and in a new day the foregoing ideas may take on a wider and deeper appeal.

One possible pragmatic value which may accompany the more general acceptance of the theory of emergent evolution and the application of gestalt principles in the field of social phenomena is that such an application may lead to a more experimental and empirical attitude. In the field of social problems our views have frequently been arrived at more by deductive reasoning than by inductive procedure. Thus, to illustrate, in order to settle certain disputed points in social policy certain "leaders of the people" will appeal to the "sacredness of the constitution," apparently supposing that the framers of this document possessed some supernatural insight enabling them to foresee all the future contingencies of an increasingly complex civilization. If the acceptance of the theory of emergent evolution would persuade politicians to settle such questions as to whether we ought to join the League of Nations by an examination of the conditions and the needs of the modern world, rather than by reference to what George Washington said about the necessity of avoiding "entangling alliances" with foreign nations, this might well justify the acceptance of the doctrine of emergent evolution as applied to social phenomena.

II. Social Gestalten

Some individuals will object to the last paragraph on the ground that it is a prostitution of the theory of emergent evolution. But that the extension of the theory of emergence and gestalt psychology to social processes is not a misapplication is what I hope to show now. In order to do this it is necessary to return to the organismic theory of society.

The analogy of society to an organism is an old one. St. Paul—to go no further back—considered a community to be like an organism: Ye are all members one of another. "If one member suffer all members suffer with it; if one member rejoice all members rejoice with it" (I *Cor.* xii). A somewhat different version of the organismic analogy was given by Francis Bacon, who pointed out that no body can be healthful without exercise, and then argued that a civil war is like the heat of fever; but a foreign war is like the heat of exercise, and serves to keep the body politic in health. Several centuries after Bacon, when the Darwinian theory of evolution filled the scientist's mind, there was an extension of evolutionary ideas to social processes, so that extensive use was made of the analogies between the evolution of

organisms and the evolution of societies. Herbert Spencer
made much use of the analogy. He tells us,[6] "A social
organism is like an individual organism in these essential traits: that it grows; that while growing it becomes
more complex, its parts acquire increasing mutual dependence; that its life is immense in length compared
with the lives of its component units; . . . that in both
cases there is increased integration accompanied by increasing heterogeneity." To these analogies it might be
added that cultures and races resemble organisms in that
they seem to have their periods of youth, maturity and
old age, in the end to pass away (so Oswald Spengler
says) and make room for new social organisms. On this
matter it is at least interesting to note that after T. B.
Robertson showed that the curve of growth is an S-
curve, and applies to plants, animals and the growth of
bacteria in a culture, Raymond Pearl[7] proceeded to extend this idea to the growth of human populations, supposing that each country fits into the S-curve at some
point.[8]

It is undoubtedly true that the post-Darwinian enthu-
siasts[9] pushed their ideas in this field too far. There followed, therefore, a reaction against the use of the organi-
cist view in society, which then fell into disrepute. But
some ideas seem to possess the secret of the Phœnix, for
they come back to life again. Among those who may be
referred to as being sympathetic with this revived organismic view are the contemporary European scientists
Friederich Alverdes and Pareto, whom we have already

[6] *Autobiography,* ii, p. 56; see also his *Principles of Ethics.*
[7] "The Growth of Populations," *Quarterly Review of Biology,* Dec. 1927.
[8] On this matter see also W. C. Allee's *Animal Aggregations,* the University of Chicago Press.
[9] In this group we find: P. Lilienfeld, *Zur Verteidigung der organ-
ischen Methode in der Sociologie* (1898); R. Worms, *Organisme et so-
ciété* (1896); J. Novicow, *Conscience et volonté sociale* (1897).

referred to. According to Alverdes,[10] "Mass psychology, as is well-known, proves the truth of the dictum that the whole is not merely the sum of its parts. In other words, the collective effect, obtained by the coöperation of individuals, can never be inferred from the mere summation of individual achievements. Thus the mass, or collective action M, cannot be ascertained by adding together the single actions of the individuals, A, B, C; their coöperation produces a result *sui generis*. The equation then is not

$$M = f(A) + f(B) + f(C)$$
$$\text{but} \quad M = f(A, B, C) \text{ "}$$

According to this authority, this principle is illustrated in colonies of ants, bees, wasps, etc., and applies to such functions or cultural patterns as singing, pugnacity, panics, etc.

Among the American leaders of this revival of the organismic theory of society is Professor Charles M. Child, the eminent biologist. Child speaks of an organism as "a more or less definite and discrete order and unity, in other words a pattern, which not only determines its structure and the relation of the parts to each other, but enables it to act as a whole with respect to the world about it." [11] He tells us that "The organism is a dynamic order, pattern, or integration among living systems or units. A social organization is exactly the same thing." [12] In considering the difficulties with this view Professor Child points out:

[10] *Social Life in the Animal World*, p. 14.
[11] *The Physiological Foundations of Behavior*, 1924, p. 1.
[12] *Ibid.*, p. 270.

Objections such as those that human society is not a big animal, that it has, for example, no stomach, no muscles, etc., etc., are just as true of many organisms as for society. It has been said that the social mind has no sensorium. But do not individuals in relation to each other and to the environment constitute the sensorium of the social mind just as truly as cells and cell groups in relation to each other and to the external world constitute the sensorium of the individual mind?

Professor Child has carried these ideas over into the field of sociology in an article on the "Biological Foundations of Social Integration," [13] in which he argues that "Integration is not a mere aggregation of units, but rather the development of different relations between them. The relations, not the parts, are the integrating factors."

Professor Child is well known as the outstanding advocate of the doctrine of *physiological gradients*. In the organism, according to him, the direction and rate of growth is controlled by centers of higher metabolism, these centers exercising dominance over other regions. The gestalt psychologists have insisted that physiological gradients are true gestalten, and Child has not demurred. Now if we accept this analogy between an organism and society, what is true of the individual organism is also true of the social organism, so that we would expect social patterns to embody levels of dominance and subordination, the entire whole illustrating an organismic gestalt.

That social or cultural patterns or gestalten exhibit the characteristics of wholes which are the expression of the dynamic interaction of the part-processes is illustrated by W. M. Wheeler's work on social insects. Similar social integrations of an organismic type appear on the human level. One investigator, R. D. MacKenzie,

[13] *American Sociological Society Publications,* 1928, Vol. 12, 26-42.

in an article on "The Concept of Dominance and World Organization," [14] argues that "The spatial distribution of human beings and institutions is not accidental. On the contrary, it is a product of evolution and represents a dynamic functional interrelationship in which the units are organized around centers or points of dominance. The pattern is not unlike that of the living organism, which, as Child points out, is a vital integration of organs, cells, and tissues functioning in harmony with centers of dominance. Moreover, human, like biological evolution, reveals an ongoing tendency toward a more specialized and refined relation between the centers of dominance and the subordinate integrated parts. The development of communication is rapidly transforming the world from the smaller, undifferentiated, symmetrical unit of spatial distribution into the highly centralized and specialized axiated pattern."

In the field of popular belief, the idea that the group as such has some sort of reality reflects itself in such common expressions as the "genius of a people" the "spirit of the times," and so on. The danger in using such expressions is that they may lead to the creation of such entities as the "group mind," which, by hypostatization, then secure a detached and mystical existence. To avoid such misconceptions it is necessary to keep in mind that we are always dealing with modes of behavior; our terms refer to functional integrations and not to "things."

And now it is well for us to indicate the value these ideas may have in helping us deal with certain problems of social science. One problem of sociology and anthropology arises in connection with the question of the relation between the individual and the social group. Are human purposes real forces in society? Is individual ini-

[14] *The American Journal of Sociology,* 1927, Vol. 28.

tiative actually potent in changing the course of social evolution? Or is the group dominant, imposing its social laws of evolution upon the individuals, who therefore merely reflect the social-environmental conditions and institutions? Why in fact *do* social patterns change in the course of time? What is the origin of the new social gestalt? All these questions are phases of the problem of cultural determinism.

These problems come into existence in their present form as a result of the formulation of the concept of *culture*. This concept, when first formulated, promised to be useful in the analysis of social processes. The idea, as E. B. Tylor pointed out, refers to the tool-using, institution-making, and value-realizing activities of human beings. It will be noted that in this sense human groups possess culture but animal societies do not.

The adoption of this concept then gave rise to such questions as these: How did these cultures of different groups arise? And what makes them change and evolve? We seem to be in a dilemma: If the group superimposes its cultural patterns on individuals, how can new cultural patterns arise as these patterns are transmitted, through the media of social heredity, from generation to generation? If, on the contrary, individuals are the source of the new social mutation, the novel cultural patterns, where do these innovators, these creative individuals, get their ideas?

In formulating answers to these questions social scientists find it difficult to agree with each other. The differences of opinion between various "schools" amounts almost to chaos. According to the school of cultural anthropologists who have adopted a "cultural determinism" as an explanation of social phenomena, the cultural achievements of human beings are always determined by previous cultures. Since, according to this view, cultural transmission and change is a group phenomenon, we need not appeal to individual psychology to explain social processes. But other historical sociologists and anthropologists are sceptical about this cultural determinism. They hold that individual personalities are genuine factors in the social processes. According to this view, the cause of a social phenomenon is never another social phenomenon alone, but a combination of social and individual processes.

And now let us consider what appears to be the proper attitude towards these matters from the point of view of the emergent evolution of cultural gestalten. We set down the following principles:

1. The origin of new ideas and practises has its inception in the exceptional individuals of the social group. This individual inventiveness is to be explained in terms of the tendency towards variation present in some degree in all living matter. These mutations are usually the more extreme fluctuations about the mean (social norm) of a statistical ensemble (society).

2. There is the fixation or establishment of a few such competing and coöperating variations, and those that survive become the cultural traits of the group.

3. There is a transmission of such traits or patterns to succeeding generations through social heredity. There may be a communication of these patterns to neighboring groups. That is, the same process goes on between adjacent groups (tribes, races, etc.) that goes on within each group. This process is known as the "diffusion of culture."

The rate of variation is probably related to the number of sub-groups within a larger group. A homogeneous and isolated group or community is always backward, conservative, and unprogressive. The cultural patterns are then relatively stable over a considerable period of time. Contact with groups having different customs and conventions helps to break down the folk-ways of any group. Cultural divergencies are like "impurities" in chemical processes, which act as catalytic agents.

Probably the great majority of mutations are wasted, in the sense that they do not become stabilized in society. Professor Punnett has calculated that if the population contains .001% of a new variety, and if the variety has even 5% selective advantage over the original form, this form will completely disappear in less than 100 generations. I see no reason why a similar estimate should not hold for cultural variations. It is difficult in some cases to see what the test of an advantage in the struggle for existence can mean in social evolution, but at least it is clear that the small statistical fluctuations will in time produce new patterns.

If the social pattern is a true emergent, there is a carrying forward of some of the old elements, but these are modified in the new whole produced. Since there is a relatively permanent psychological structure to human nature (because of heredity, in the form of "instincts," inherited mental traits, if any, etc.), at least as compared with the relatively fast rate of social change, this psychological substratum in human nature will provide a check upon excessive social variability. And the continuity of cultural evolution will be due to the stabilization and transmission of those socially acquired characteristics which are the cultural gestalten of the group.

In a sense the origin of the new social pattern is still unexplained. In biology we have the parallel problem: How explain the origin of a new structure, e.g., the eye or ear? Is the eye an adaptation to a previously operating stimulus? But this overlooks the fact that the stimulus does not exist for the organism until the organism has found a mechanism selectively tuned to respond to the stimulus. The writer [15] has previously posed the question, Does not the organism create the environment as much as the environment creates the organism that responds to it? If so, is it not clear that the physiologist's conception of the *circular reaction arcs* may be of assistance in helping us to understand the situation? Certainly these two, the organism and the environment, play into each other in such a subtle and intricate way that it is difficult to tell where the one leaves off and the other begins. In connection with our problem of the origin of social mutations we find that the notion of circular reaction arcs has been applied by Healy, and we quote his own words:

If we observe our cases with an eye to the dynamics of the situation we are inexorably led step by step further to witness the fact that the environment plays upon and modifies the individual and, what is usually not set forth, the individual plays upon and modifies the environment. Then, as modified by each other, they act upon each other again, each reacting to the new situation,—this is a conception that has taken hold of social and political science as well as psychology.[16]

Thus through the interaction of the internal and the external, the individual and the social, a new type of behavior, perhaps also a new type of structure, emerges.

In bringing the present chapter to a close we summarize the viewpoint in the following way.

[15] Cf. *The Alchemy of Light and Color,* The New Science Series.
[16] Quoted from Branham's paper, *loc. cit.*

III. The Creative Aspect of Nature

The puzzling feature of nature, sometimes regarded as the exclusive characteristic of the organic world, is its ability to rise above the source, so to speak,—to produce new species, new levels endowed with increasingly larger supplies of potential energy. But this notion that the stream of life runs uphill, in seeming opposition to the general tendency of energy in the inorganic world to run down hill and dissipate itself in a homogeneous distribution, overlooks the fact that in the inorganic world the tendency is present in no less degree for behavior-complexes to produce more complicated organizations containing more abundant stores of potential energy. Thus atoms, molecules, and complexes of inorganic molecules are all reservoirs of energy. The difference between the organic world and the inorganic world in this matter consists in the fact that in organisms the energies are more labile; the organism is an equilibrium under stress, so that the stimulus may act as a "trigger" effect in releasing the available energies.

This last fact is undoubtedly related to the peculiar nature of the carbon atom, which, because of its valency or ability to combine with other chemical elements, possesses the property of entering into the intricate molecular patterns necessary to form the different types of protoplasm. It is for this reason that the chemistry of life is to a large extent the chemistry of carbon compounds.

An explanation of the tendency of inorganic matter to aggregate into stable complexes is offered by G. N. Lewis.[17] Professor Lewis tells us that it would not be far from the truth to state that nearly every chemical

17 In his book, *Valence and the Structure of Matter*, 1923.

process occurs in such a way as to increase the net amount of conjugation. By conjugation is meant the partial neutralization of the molecular magnetic fields. Electrons, he says, conjugate to produce a couple which is self-contained magnetically, possessing little residual magnetic field. This reminds one of one of the principles of gestalt psychology, that a "good" configuration is one that satisfies certain conditions of energy-distribution: the configurative energy is at a minimum. The gestalt psychologists believe that they see configurational principles at work in embryological development, and if there is any valid analogy between ontogenetic embryological development and phylogenetic evolution, as Haeckel's famous biogenetic law would lead us to suppose, this suggests that configurative principles are also at work in exercising appropriate effects in the evolutionary process.

In explaining the evolutionary process biologists find it necessary to discriminate between the *productive* and the *selective* agencies at work in nature. In the last analysis, however, both of these must be traced back to the environment. And the further science progresses the clearer it becomes that the environment to be considered is not only social (in the case of human beings), but terrestrial and cosmic as well. There is reason to believe that the radiations emitted by radioactive substances in the earth produce mutations in near-by plants, the changes thus produced sensitizing the plant to new types of environmental stimuli. Perhaps something of the same sort holds for animals. Perhaps not only radium emanations, but cosmic and other radiations from the sun and the depths of space, enter at different stages in the evolution of living organisms to supply the activating energy which alters the hereditary characteristics of living forms, producing—as R. S. Lillie has suggested—those extreme fluctuations in the Brownian (statistical) movements of the colloidal particles of the genes (hereditary determiners) which appear as mutations. Thus the *productive* agency, no less than the *selective* agency, responsible for the upward trend of evolution is not in defiance of the laws of nature, but in coöperation with them.

An illustration of this cosmic "coöperation" is seen in the case of plants, where we have what is called an *energy-couple*. In the building up of more complex compounds through the photo-synthetic reaction we have an example of a process which appears to violate the principle that energy tends to be dissipated and become available. Here water and carbon dioxide react together, utilizing the degrading energy of sunlight, to produce carbohydrates, an available source of energy for the animals that eat the plants. But, as James Johnstone [18] points out, while starch accumulates in the green leaf exposed to sunlight, "the *whole* system is the green leaf + CO_2 and OH_2 + the degrading sunlight. In the system thus defined entropy increases very slowly. The system is one in which there are *coupled* energy transformations, (1) the degrading sunlight, and (2) the photo-synthetic process. If there were no coupling, the solar energy would degrade, with maximum entropy increase; if there is a coupling, the entropy increase becomes minimal." In the light of such considerations does it not seem likely that further knowledge concerning the causes of developing life will reveal more such coupled energy transformations? An affirmative answer to this question may throw more light upon the biological problem of the origin of mutations.

[18] Cf. *The Mechanism of Life*, London, 1921, p. 221.

It is important to note that as organic evolution proceeds there arises in nature not only more complicated organisms, but an expanding environment. In order to find outlets for their energies complicated organisms must find or create more complicated environments with which they may enter into reciprocal relations. Potentialities are brought out or given expression by one system entering into dynamic intercourse with other systems, and as a result of the emergence of a new set of relations the organism is sensitized to new stimuli. Nature is a system of systems, all of them only relatively independent of each other. As evolution proceeds more systems contribute formative stimuli and selective agencies. The problem of producing order out of the threatening chaos is one of organization, of producing levels of dominance and subordination.

On the biological level nature has solved the problem of physiological order through the development of the central nervous system. The energy of cerebral metabolism has come to dominate sheer muscular strength, size, weight, etc., so that intelligence is now a powerful factor of advantage in the struggle for existence. Exactly the same thing is happening on the level of human civilization. Cephalization is a social as well as a biological necessity, and what we now need to do is develop a specific functional group to do for society what the brain has done for the organism. This takes us into ethics, and into the next chapter.

CHAPTER XIV

CREATIVE MORALITY

SEVERAL years ago the late George Dorsey lectured on the subject "What Price Ignorance?" In introducing his subject the lecturer asked his audience, composed of students for the most part, what they had gotten out of the various subjects they had studied. "What did you get out of sociology? Nothing! What did you get out of psychology? Nothing! What did you get out of ethics? Nothing!" Thus did one of our intellectuals epitomize the futility of present-day social science. At about the same time another well known authority of a rising school of social engineering—Stuart Chase to be exact—delivered himself of the pronouncement that in his opinion, this day of our Lord, all politics, all philosophy and sociology, and most psychology is bunk! But for those who claim to be disciples of scientific method these attitudes exhibit a deplorable lack of historical perspective, or sense of geologic time. What more can be expected of creatures who have so lately climbed down from the trees, stood erect, and taken to building civilizations? What more is to be hoped for from those creatures whom Bertrand Russell called lumps of impure carbons? If man, as a chemical compound, can be bought at the corner drug store for eighty-seven cents, what do these men want for a dollar? Considering the fact that man consists of about four buckets of water and some minerals, hasn't the human race done pretty well?

What a mechanistic-materialistic point of view overlooks is the creative aspect of nature, the fact of emergent evolution. Nature is constituted of levels in an evolutionary hierarchy. In each case certain analogies carry over from one level to another. If the thesis of emergent evolution is true, the fact of novelty makes anticipation and predictability difficult; but in spite of this we may be able to *transpose* certain principles from one level to another.[1] Another generalization which holds on all levels, except for the level of the ultimate elements of nature, is that the complexities of one level are unified into a new organic unity when the transition from one level to another occurs. This is what G. P. Conger terms "epitomization." In our own view this may be represented as follows:

```
○ ○ ○ Complex Social Groups (Nations)
  ○ ○ ○ Simple Social Groups
    ○ ○ ○ Multicellular Organisms
      ○ ○ ○ Cells (Simple Organisms)
        ○ ○ ○ Molecules
          ○ ○ ○ Atoms
```

It will be recalled from Chapter VII that there are two types of simplicity in nature: (*a*) there are *simple simplicities,* or *first order simplicities,* and (*b*) there are *complex simplicities,* or *second order simplicities.* As previously pointed out, these two types of simplicities are illustrated, respectively, by a gas and a crystal. A gas, such as the air in this room, is a first order simplicity in the sense that it is homogeneous and isotropic with re-

[1] The way in which the principles of gestalt theory make possible reasoning by analogy, thus providing the basis for scientific *insight,* is dealt with in Chapters V and VIII of the present volume. *Transposition* is a matter of *isomorphism,* or similarity of logical structure.

spect to its space dimensions; whereas a crystal is inhomogeneous and anisotropic. Now the important thing
is that nature apparently is not satisfied with first level
simplicities, but in its evolutionary progress produces
higher, or second order, simplicities.

It will be noted that complex simplicities contain relatively large supplies of potential energy capable of being released under appropriate conditions. We must also
keep in mind that in a complex living organism the
greatest amount of potential energy can be released only
by a sufficiently complex environment. In order that the
potentialities of human nature can be given expression
the individual must be responding in a variety of ways.
This leads us to the further observation that *we human
beings tend to react to the most complicated environment we can meaningfully simplify.* In æsthetics this second order simplicity is known as unity-in-variety, and is
illustrated by the unifying architecture underlying the
complexity of a symphony, drama, picture, etc.

The suggestion has frequently been put forth that
human beings always take the line of least resistance.
But from the present point of view this is false. Human behavior, we suggest, is a compromise between two
laws: the one is the principle of *least action*[2] and the
other is a principle of *maximal energy expenditure*
(least potential energy or greatest entropy). The first
principle tends to result in laziness and monotony of
conduct. The second leads us to seek out and react to
new situations. The one leads us to simplify the environ-

[2] The *principle of the conservation of energy,* which, as previously
noted, appears to hold for the transformations of energy in an organism,
is a special case of the broader physical *principle of least action,* which
plays such an important part in the present doctrine of wave mechanics.
    In his book, *The Science of Psychology,* Prof. R. H. Wheeler tries to
explain all gestalt processes in terms of the principle of least action.

ment; the other leads us to complicate it. Man is a moving compromise between two opposed tendencies.

Elsewhere the writer [3] has presented the following general interpretation of evolution: Every atomic (discrete) entity of nature is set in a wider environment of energy which constitutes its field. Given a system of particles, there will be a field of potentialities which will determine what kind of configuration can be further assimilated to this stress-center. At any given time a cross section of an organism will reveal a *static* aspect, which represents what has already been accomplished, and functioning in accordance with which represents the mechanical aspect of behavior, and a *dynamic* aspect, which represents the transformations in progress. It is this nisus towards the future, the movement toward the integration of higher unities, which we designate as the teleological aspect of nature. The (relatively) static aspect we call matter, which is the bound energy serving as the "material" vehicle of these transformations in this movement towards the future. In such a view structural gestalten (or substances) are simply conventionalized energy patterns (or crystallized functional gestalten).

Throughout evolution there is a conservative force making for conformity and standardization and a radical force making for variability and novelty. In general the speeds of the processes of change which involve an energy-turnover are determined by the result of this interaction. Thus in chemistry the

$$Velocity \ of \ reaction = \frac{driving \ force}{resistance}$$

In biological evolution the resistance or conservative

[3] "A Monism of Creative Behavior," *Journal of Philosophy*, 1924, Vol. 21, 477-492.

force is heredity, and the factor of variability is mutation or novelty. Thus we may say the

$$Movement\ of\ evolution = \frac{variability\ (mutations)}{standardization\ (heredity)}$$

The function of biological evolution seems to be to produce more complex but still unified organisms. Since social evolution, in some respects, is a continuation of biological evolution, we may say that its function is to make possible the development of human individuals with a wide range of interests, capable of indulging in varied behavior, but so unified and integrated as to preserve the stability of the self. We may, if we wish, say that the goal of evolution is the production of souls, if we keep in mind as a definition of the soul the progressive synthesis of the reaction patterns of the body.

Human happiness is a result of a compromise in which there is an optimum of individual variety with a minimum of standardization, or conformity to social pattern. Continued happiness implies a progressive enlargement of our range of interests. The only goal for living matter is continued growth, and the measure of growth might be given by some "coefficient of activity," measured in terms of the conversion of potential energy into kinetic energy. Social organization makes possible a greater release of potential energy by providing the increasingly complex environment supplying the stimuli to set off the energic streams of the organism. Increasing complexity of social organization is both a cause and an effect of increasing the rate of energy expenditure. It has been calculated that a man of today has the equivalent of twenty slaves working for him. Whatever the number, in the future it is likely that this will be progressively increased to the point where an individual may approximate the power of a god.

Social evolution seems to resemble what in chemistry is called an *autocatalytic* reaction: it speeds itself up as it goes along. But how long can this last, it is asked? Surely we must eventually reach the point where we will have used up all the potential energy that is available! Not so! This is to underestimate the creative power of physics and chemistry. When ordinary chemical substances (coal and oil) no longer supply us with sufficient stores of energy we must find other, and more tremendous, stores of energy—there is always the energy of the sun awaiting some genius to harness it. By the alchemy of synthetic chemistry we can create the materials we need. And so far as the problem of food is concerned, not even the most rabid follower of Malthus can deny that creative chemistry promises much by way of artificial synthesis. This increase in the velocity and amount of energy turn-over is readily observed in the American industrial evolution. One of the speakers in G. Lowes Dickinson's book, *A Modern Symposium,* states that the god of America is acceleration. Many pious moralists look askance at our fast pace, and want to know what is the good of it if we don't know where we are going. The trouble with these persons is that they fail to realize that no man knows "where we are going." We can't tell that until we get there—which won't be for some time yet! For better or for worse, we, the "people of action," must fulfill our energetic destiny.

In this view there is no necessary antagonism between the individual and the progressively larger groups in which he is included. Standardization of the social mechanisms, specialization of function, may increase the possibility of the individual's variability of response. But we must never forget that the only function of social mechanisms is to provide individuals with greater possibilities of variable response. This is seen in international arrangements (such as passports), which make possible wider varieties of experience. In some cases standardization and convention may impede the movement towards novelty. Then standardization becomes an end in itself, instead of being a means to an end. While it is true that there is more law and more standardization today than ever before, this does not mean that we are less free or our conduct less variable than that which is possible in simpler form of social organization. To the contrary, for we can use up more energy in a wider variety of ways than could primitive man. In an increasingly complex environment novel stimuli provide new energy escapements. It is possible that man, who has been described as a space-eater and a time-binder, may some day find it necessary and possible to explore in fact, as he now explores in theory, the other corners of the universe in order to find new stimuli to provide the continually expanding environment which calls forth the conversion of potential into kinetic energy.

In all this it is obvious that the only function of standardized social structures demanding conformity is to provide the minimal conditions of coöperation so that everyone can follow out his own inclinations so far as possible. What a person's inclinations and interests are likely to be is determined in part by one's inheritance, the conservative factor that limits variability. In social standardization this hereditary factor is represented by the conventionalized patterns of response crystallized into what are called the *mores*, or folkways, and legal codes. Just as in the individual growth results from a compromise between new elements assimilated into and gradually transforming the old, already established, substratum, so social evolution results from the modification of the old order to meet new situations.

Ethicists distinguish two levels of morality, the level of customary morality and the level of reflective morality. We see that a certain amount of standardization is necessary in order to run a society. But the conventionalized patterns must not be held sacred merely because they have the sanction of our ancestors; they must be modified to meet the demands of a people who are living in a rapidly evolving society. The persons who are working along the frontiers of this advance, recreating our moral codes, are usually regarded as heretics, radicals, etc., because they criticize and tear down the old patterns of thought and practise. On the other hand, we recognize that we are living in a risky universe, where there is a real possibility of smashing the entire machinery through some unfortunate radical social experiment, so that there must be a limit to our tolerations of excessive variability from the statistical norm. The problem of morality arises in its most critical form at this very point.

Granted that the moral concepts and actions achieved by previous generations are not sacred, and that individuals must strike out in new directions, what ought to be the limits of mutation away from social conformity? In order to have complex simplicity in our social organization some social standardization is absolutely essential. And yet in order to grow and progress we cannot stand still. We therefore seem forced to condemn a man or a society if it changes too fast or if it does not change fast enough. As a problem in social dynamics the question is, What is the best speed of social evolution? What is the best balance between radicalism (variability) and conservatism (standardization)? How can we carry over from tradition and custom the best elements without the worst? To answer these questions would require more knowledge and ability than the present writer possesses.

So far as the problem of individual ethics is concerned, it seems to me that morality here consists in acting in conformity with the mores and the laws of the state, in observing conventional patterns of conduct, so long as reason tells the thinking individual that the customary standards are still useful, and in departing from these social habits when reason tells the individual that they have outlived whatever usefulness they have had in the past. There are several possible criticisms to be made of this conception of morality. For one thing, it seems to open the way to an individual's justifying any kind of conduct; in other words, it seems to open the gates to the wholesale "rationalization" of all sorts of selfishness and immorality. Replying to this criticism, it may be argued that the dangers from this source are not nearly as great as this criticism would have us believe; however, insofar as it is a true statement of what is likely to happen, it must be admitted that this is one of the chances we must take. Another criticism of such a theory of morality is that it is too abstract, and does not tell us what to do in specific situations. Does it, for example, permit one to break the law, if one honestly comes to the conclusion that the law is unjust or antiquated? I do not think it possible or desirable to lay down general rules to cover all cases; but it is obvious that this conception does call for a wide margin of freedom in the right to criticize the established order of things.

We must recognize, furthermore, that when an individual effects a modification of any of our standardized mechanisms only the verdict of history as the thing is tried out experimentally can tell us whether this was the right line of advance. Of course, we can, and ought, to learn by past experience and by the social experiments being made at the present time by other governments. We ought, for instance, to watch with the same interest which the chemist has in observing the new and significant experiments of chemistry the social experiments now being made in Russia, always asking ourselves what these results have to teach us. Since the reaction has not yet gone to "completion," we must suspend judgment about some matters for a while. It is obvious that in this view we do not accept any of the concepts of religion, science, or politics as final and absolute; we are always willing to revise our ideas as new facts and discoveries necessitate. From this point of view the problem of education becomes that of developing plasticity of mind and intellectual honesty—the ability to adapt one's self to new ideas with sufficient insight into the values and defects of new and old ideas so that we get variability without disaster and standardization without stagnation.

A third objection to the present view is that no place is provided for making qualitative distinctions between various types of behavior. Since we seem to have only the quantitative criterion of maximal energy-turnover, one type of behavior would seem to be just as good as another provided it gave expression to an equal quantity of energy. In reply it is pointed out that the goodness of an act lies in the extent to which it lends itself to the processes of biological integration and social synthesis. It is no doubt true that integration (construction) of the new involves disintegration (destruction) of the old, but that does not invalidate the statement. With Aristotle we may well insist that all possible types of response, all innate potentialities, should be given expression. The only ethical restriction to conduct is imposed by the demand for unity of function of the organism. Intelligence is the necessary instrument through which this inner harmony and coördination of behavior is secured.

It is, therefore, not merely the quantity of energy expended which is the test of ethical behavior. A work of art is great in proportion to the extent to which it gives expression to all our capacities for experience *with the least effort*. Beethoven's Ninth Symphony, like a powerful but compact automobile, gives us the greatest achievement with the least waste. And so life, itself a kind of symphonic organization, should contain within itself richness and harmony. From this point of view no action is wrong in itself; any act becomes immoral when it interferes with growth, in ourselves or in others.

Since biological progress has been in the direction of substituting brain for brawn, it seems logical to conclude that in order to continue and facilitate this movement in the field of social evolution it will be necessary to encourage a sublimation of the instinctive and emotional cravings of mankind into the channels usually termed the "higher" activities. It is a commonplace that the world is becoming more closely knit as time goes on; there is an increasingly greater interdependence of function in the social organism. Since no nation liveth unto itself, and since the world can solve its economic and political problems only through what Kropotkin called "mutual aid," there must necessarily be produced a machinery for improved international coöperation. This means that eventually the nations of the world will have to evolve for the social organism the same sort of center of intellectual dominance which nature evolved for individual organisms when she produced the cerebral hemispheres, the vehicle of highest metabolic rate and dominance. Until such a new level of social synthesis and energic sublimation is achieved, our aspirations will continue to suffer defeat through lack of an organ to centralize, control and unify the complexity of function of the social organism.

A few years ago the slogan, "back to normalcy," represented the attitude of mind of most of our politicians and industrial leaders. What such an epimethean attitude totally fails to grasp is the basic fact of evolution, and this in spite of the prevalent lip service to the ideal of "progress." The simple fact is that post-World War civilization has reached a critical point in its evolutionary career. Inane platitudes will not exorcise a difficult situation. Fundamental changes in theory and practise, and not pious hopes for world-saviors, can cure social maladjustments. A new technique for social control, guided by a humanistic religion, must replace the long standing practises of the "old deal." The mechanical ability and business shrewdness of a Henry Ford is helpless in the face of a situation requiring a readjustment of our notions concerning the place of wealth in society, the obligations of nations to common humanity, and so on. When one surveys the present status of the human race, with its institutional, racial, and impending national conflicts, it becomes clear that the potentialities of human intelligence may well be drained to the point of exhaustion, before men learn to secure that harmony of coördination which is necessary if the social organism is to survive.

CHAPTER XV

THE SOCIAL OBJECTIVES OF HUMANISM

I. Religion Versus Ethics

THE modern world is utilitarian in its attitudes. Unlike the mediæval world, it does not take its traditions, ideals, and institutions for granted. This practical interest leads men to judge all customs and institutions in terms of their human value, here and now, in serving the needs of the social order. Modern utilitarianism is "this worldly" and not "other worldly." Thus it comes about that the label, "made in heaven,"—one attached to time-honored beliefs and practises—no longer suffices to guarantee their social value.

One of the most interesting manifestations of social utilitarianism is found in our changing attitude towards religion. The question, formerly never posed, of whether religion is a blessing or a curse to the human race is now frequently discussed. The reply which is usually given to this question by disputants is categorical—it is either "yes" or "no." But such an answer seems to me to represent the wrong method of approach. It is quite probable that no generalization can be made which will cover all cases.

It is all a question of how religion functions. Religion is a valuable asset to society when it contributes to moral development, and becomes a curse when it hinders this, or positively fosters anti-moral tendencies. This view that religion may in some cases be immoral may come as a shock to some persons, especially those who hold that the source and sanction of all moral principles is to be found in religion, or in God conceived as the ultimate foundation of all morality. Orthodox religion holds that morality issues from a supernatural source and presupposes a cosmic power working for righteousness. Without raising the more fundamental question of the necessity of theism as a basis for morality, let us here merely recall that such a view usually is based on the idea of a *revealed* truth, as found, for example, in the doctrine of the "verbal inspiration" of holy literature, and that the foil to this idea of the necessity for a theistic basis for moral conduct is found in the actual history of any religion, which shows that moral principles evolve, developing under the guidance of changing environmental conditions, new experiences, etc. There is therefore the constant necessity for reinterpreting the utterances of the prophets and founders of such religions. This is illustrated by the history of Judaism and Christianity, no less than by the history of other supposedly revealed religions, and presents difficulties to the acceptance of the supernatural theory of the origin of specific moral principles.

In order to clarify the above view that religion may be either an asset or a liability to a social system, depending on how it functions, let us briefly outline what morality is conceived to involve when it is thus freed from its traditional religious moorings.

In accordance with the view of some moralists we here assume that in any act capable of moral evaluation there are two aspects of conduct to be considered: (*a*) the *motive* or *intention* behind the act, and (*b*) the results or consequences of the act. An act, in order to be moral or immoral, must be a result of a conscious choice; it must be voluntary and purposive. (The acceptance of a behavioristic psychology does not invalidate this statement.) Any person not capable of such action is non-moral; thus the behavior of imbeciles, idiots, morons in some measure, insane persons, and children is neither moral nor immoral—it is amoral. It must be noted, however, that the question of the place of rewards and punishment is not to be determined solely in terms of responsibility for the acts committed, since there is also involved the question of whether praise and blame modifies the future conduct of such non-moral individuals.

A good act, therefore, is one which is inspired by a good motive, voluntarily chosen. A good motive is one which is inspired by a feeling of good will, or by love. It is a simple fact of introspective psychology that some of our acts spring from feelings of kindness, sympathy, and the like, while others are the manifestations of fear, anger, jealousy, and the desire to harm others. To be good one must have generous motives, a subjective attitude of desire to benefit others.

This, however, is not the whole story. The road to hell is paved with good intentions, and many a well-intentioned but ill-resulting action has been excused on the ground that "I meant well." The other aspect of conduct, without which no action is fully moral, is that the act must lead to the right objective results, or socially desirable consequences. What "good" consequences are is not easy to state, but in general those actions which contribute to social progress satisfy that demand. To indicate briefly what is meant by this it may be stated that progress towards a more ideal social order involves at least two things: (a) the creation of a condition in which each person who is willing to work is guaranteed the minimal requirements of food, shelter, and clothing, and (b) the development of social institutions which make it possible for every person to find outlets for his particular talents and interests. In general an ideal society would be one in which each person had enough to do of the sort of thing he likes to do, and can do, to make life zestful. Such a world does not exist today, but it is certainly not beyond hope of realization.

No one, to my knowledge, has worked out the possible combinations of acts, on the assumption that every moral act has two aspects, subjective and objective, each of which in turn can be either good or bad. The scheme is quite simple. If g stands for good, and b for bad, and M stands for motives and C for consequences, we can construct the following four classes of acts:

Mg Cg—Social legislation; intelligent philanthropy, etc.
Mg Cb—Prohibitory laws of misguided reformers.
Mb Cg—Desire to harm, but unwittingly do good.
Mb Cb—Assassination of a valuable leader.

The reader can undoubtedly add many illustrations to this list of examples.

It would be an interesting question to debate whether more harm is done by unintelligent but well-meaning reformers, or by clever but ill-motivated criminals, but this is beyond the scope of the present volume. It is obvious that the person of highest moral character is the person of the first type—an individual of benevolent impulses, or good motives, with sufficient intelligence to foresee the consequences of his acts and choose courses of action that lead to socially beneficial results. Of course no man is omniscient, and in a complex society even the most farseeing will make mistakes. But certainly the view expressed in the statement, "be good, sweet maid, and let those who will be wise," is herewith shown to be false, for the sweet maid could not be "good" unless she were wise. Here we agree with Socrates when he asserts a close relation between intelligence and morality.

And now we ask, what has this to do with religion? The answer is that religion has frequently taken the wrong stand on social problems and thereby assisted the forces making for immorality. Orthodox religion claims to be founded on revelation, and this means that it must look backwards in time to past patterns of belief and "upward" in space to transcendental sources for its ideals, and thereby obstructs the intelligent discussion of social problems in terms of their consequences in this world. The attitude of orthodox denominationalism on questions of marriage, birth control, economic problems, medical research, the teachings of science, etc., is frequently ultra-conservative and opposed to social and intellectual progress. To be sure, religious leaders occasionally do become more radical and demand more progressive forms of social justice, but these instances are in the minority.

Religion, then, in itself is neither a benefit nor a curse to the human race. It depends on how it functions. If it looks backwards, is ultra-conservative, and obstructs the free analysis of moral issues it is a curse; if it fosters intelligence and holds up unselfish motives for conduct it is wholesome. With respect to the influence of religion in the past, I shall not venture an estimate of whether the Hebrew-Christian religious tradition has been beneficial or harmful to Western European culture. I am here primarily concerned with the present and the future. This we do know: churches are going concerns; billions of dollars are invested in religious institutions; and millions of people are loyal to their respective faiths. Such a powerful institution of society cannot readily be abolished. But it surely can be changed, provided religion becomes sufficiently flexible to readjust itself. Freed from supernaturalism, fostering such ideals as love and the brotherhood of man, religion could be an effective instrument in the development of the proper subjective attitudes in conduct. But the evaluation of the goodness or badness of acts in terms of social consequences must be taken out of the field of authority, tradition, and revelation, and put within the domain of intelligent consideration. It is the business of a science of ethics to formulate a program of social reform, and religion will have to learn to take its social objectives from moral science. This is simply a plea for a humanistic religion, and if this transition from fundamentalism to humanism does not take place religion very likely will become another of the fossils of cultural evolution. If we cannot reshape religion so that it supplies the emotional drive for social reform, working toward a super-national and super-racial social order, then indeed orthodox religion will become its own Anti-Christ!

And now let us see what humanism holds out in the way of a positive program of social reform.

II. HUMANISM AND SOCIAL PROGRESS

The problem we now turn our attention to is that of stating more explicitly the social objectives of humanism. In other words we are here attempting to outline briefly the position of the Humanist on certain contemporary social issues.

At the very outset it is necessary to remind ourselves of an elementary logical principle, namely, that any discussion of social implications must be guided by our definition of the term "humanism." The first desideratum, therefore, is a formulation of the meaning of the term as it is here understood. Obviously humanism conceived after the fashion of Irving Babbitt is not the same as that set forth in the *Humanist Manifesto*. And the social implications of the two will necessarily differ according to the differences in the fundamental characteristics of the two conceptions.

The point of view from which the present survey is made is that presented by the *Humanist Manifesto*.[1] This is not the literary humanism of Paul Elmer More. Let it not be forgotten that no one group or individual has the right to preëmpt the use of this term or monopolize its meaning. In cases where disputes arise over the right to the exclusive use of titles and tags, historical priority usually furnishes one guide for arbitration. If, following this principle, we look to the meaning of the term humanism in its historical context—the humanism of the Renaissance—it will be found, I believe, that the humanism of the *Humanist Manifesto* emphasizes the same dominant notes which prevailed in Renaissance humanism. The only emendation we have made comes in at the point where, as in the foregoing pages, we associate humanism with our own version of the theory of emergent evolution.

What are the constituent elements common to both forms of humanism? In answering this question it needs to be kept in mind that the formulation of a definition of humanism at the same time determines the nature of the social implications which can be deduced from such a definition.

[1] This Manifesto is reproduced in the author's brochure, *Humanism and New World Ideals,* published by the Antioch Press, Yellow Springs, Ohio.

The characteristics of humanism as we are here using the term are as follows:

(1). Humanism represents the belief that reason is the only method and tool for obtaining knowledge and finding solutions to our problems. Humanism is therefore opposed to the following: (a) the theological doctrine of the verbal inspiration of religious literature; (b) the belief in intuition, revelation, or any other non-rational source of knowledge; and (c) the idea that institutional authority, traditions, or conventions provide an infallible guide for belief and action.

(2). Humanism represents the belief that nature is self-sufficient and self-contained and as worthy an object of reverence as man will ever know. Humanism is opposed to the belief in miracles, special providences, and the intervention of supernatural agencies.

(3). Humanism represents a faith in human potentialities. Humanism is anthropocentric rather than theocentric.

(4). Humanism represents a faith in democracy and the instrumentalities of representative government. It believes that the use of intelligence, cultivated and made aggressive through a socially enlightened public school system, can solve the problems of evolving society as it moves into unprecedented situations and novel problems.

Summarizing these characteristics in a more concise form, we arrive at the following definition: *Humanism is the doctrine that men, through the use of intelligence, directing the institutions of democratic government, can create for themselves, without aid from "supernatural powers," a rational civilization in which each person enjoys economic security and finds cultural outlets for whatever normal human capacities and creative energies he possesses.*

Now let us consider some of the consequences of the acceptance of this definition of humanism.

I. In the first place this means that ethics must be freed from its theological background, so that moral issues are considered without reference to such debatable matters as the immortality of the soul or the existence of god. This means that no institution subscribing to such beliefs (*e.g.,* the Church) has the right to prescribe what attitude human beings shall take on moral issues, such as prohibitions, birth control, censorship, and so on.

II. This definition of humanism condemns any form of society which makes impossible the free discussion of all issues. On this score Fascism as it is observed in action in Europe fails to meet the demands of the humanistic program and therefore stands condemned.

III. In its program of social reform humanism favors a democratic government which progressively refashions itself through legislative procedure. Thus, given a society which functions according to the formulæ of democratic government, revolution is banned as a method of securing a larger measure of social justice. Insofar as communism, syndicalism, etc., advocate direct action, violence, or revolution as a method of social change, they are opposed to humanism. Any appeal to force is an abandonment of the principle of free debate and reasonable persuasion as a method of rectifying social ills.

In making this statement we assume that we have a democratic state, or a state which by further legislative enactment could be made democratic. But if we have a state in which the institutions of democracy are not in effect, revolutionary procedure designed to institute such a state would seem to have humanistic sanction, provided it can be demonstrated that this is the only method of obtaining the desired end. Whether, in these United States, we do in fact have a genuine democracy, and, if not, what steps we need to take to make it so, is a question that humanists need to consider.

IV. It is also clear that humanism stands for a greater measure of industrial democracy than our present system embodies. The NIRA provided an illustration of an attempt at achieving a more socialized and humanized community. Such efforts at social coöperation at the outset are experimental and mistakes are inevitable. Moreover it is also true that we need to bring our "New Deals" up to date every so often. It is also clear that our traditional "rugged individualism" is a thing of the past, and that any future definition of liberty that may be given must take into account the fact that the "profit motive" will have to be supplemented by other incentives, if it is not to be eliminated entirely.

The foregoing formulations appear to be valid and necessary implications of the present definition of humanism. It is probable, however, that this statement of deductions is incomplete. The following list of possible implications is therefore furnished for purposes of suggesting further possible consequences of humanism:

THE SOCIAL OBJECTIVES OF HUMANISM

I. SOCIAL RELATIONS

1. Equality of opportunity according to capacity
2. Abolition of institutional authority in fixing beliefs
3. Modernization of courts and legal procedure
4. Minimizing of crime and political dishonesty
5. Equal rights for women
6. Social equality for all races
7. Sterilization of defectives unfit to be parents

314 PHILOSOPHY AND THE SOCIAL SCIENCES

8. Abolition of capital punishment
9. Socialized medical care

II. THE FAMILY

1. Eugenics
2. Birth control
3. Abolition of child labor
4. Divorce by mutual consent
5. Removal of illegitimacy stigma
6. Old age pensions

III. EDUCATION

1. Abolition of illiteracy
2. Education for the rational use of leisure
3. Elevation of standards in the radio, movies, literature, etc.
4. Mental hygiene facilities (clinics) for all
5. Minimal intelligence tests for voters
6. Information tests for public officials, legislators, etc.
7. Development of respect for civil liberties

IV. ECONOMIC RELATIONS

1. Unemployment insurance
2. Government ownership of public utilities
3. Unionization of labor and collective bargaining
4. Coöperative movement
5. Capital tax and tax on unearned wealth

V. INTERNATIONAL RELATIONS

1. Cancellation of War Debts
2. World Disarmament
3. Abolition of nationalism and economic imperialism
4. Coöperation with League of Nations and World Court

It would, of course, be easy to criticize the above groupings. The classes of propositions are not exclusive of each other and there is some overlapping of fields of application. Furthermore, whether one accepts or rejects certain of these propositions depends upon the precise meanings assigned to them. But since, after all, humanism encourages individual reflection on these matters, it is the privilege of each professed humanist to draw his own conclusions about these, and other, possible implications of humanism. And this, let us not forget, is entirely in accordance with the democratic principles of humanism as that term has here been defined and used. Thus humanism is recommended as the best gospel of social reform consistent with the method and the results of modern science.

INDEX

A

Adams, N. K., chemist, 153
Additivity, definition of, 130
Ahrimanes (Power of Darkness), 214
Ahura Mazda (God of Light), 214
Alexander, S., British philosopher, his formula of space and time, 175; on doctrine of emergence, 276
Animism, its view of human nature, 14
Anthropomorphism, 11, 14; in poetry, 15; in relation to mechanics and relativity, 22
Arcs, circular reaction, 287
Arrhenius, Svanté, Swedish chemist, 162
Astral worship, 204, 212
Astronomy, conclusions of modern, 136
Atomism, forerunner of materialism, 67; theories on, 145
Atoms, 40 *et seq.*
Attraction of forces, in brain, 141
Augustine, St., his spiritual interpretation of history, 219
Avey, A. E., on logos doctrine, 215

B

Bacon, Francis, founder of modernism, 4; on vision, 80; organismic analogy by, 279
Bacon, Roger, 79
Baly, E. C. C., 106, 165, 166; on formaldehyde, 196
Barnes, Harry Elmer, iconoclastic views of religion by, 189
Bartley, Prof. S. H., views on neurones of, 182
Baudelaire, quoted, 15, 16
Behavior, emergence of unitary, 273; life and mind as modes of, 273, 274; tests of ethical, 302
Behaviorism, 10, 44, 183, 268; its attitude towards physics, 47
Bergson, Henri, 19; his theory of mechanism, 124; on time as a "phantom," 129
Berkeley, Bishop, idealist, philosophy of, 268
Bianci, his views on the "seat" of consciousness, 91
Biological evolution, end-result of, 174
Biology, its relation to palæopsychology, 206ff.
Bohr, theory of atom, 163
Bose, Sir Jagadis, Indian scientist, 75; on the emotions of plants, 34, 35
Botany, illustration of macroscopic pattern in, 258
Brain-patterns, 123
Branham, Dr. V. C., his formula of mass action, 233
Breasted, J. H., on ancient religions, 214, 215
Bridgman, P. W., on theory of additivity, 129
Brouwer, L. E. J., 62
Browning, Robert, quoted, 275

C

Carbon, its part in chemistry of consciousness, 166; importance of shape, 168
Carbon atom, valency of, 288
Catalytic processes, 150
Cephalization, 291
Chemistry, most effectual agent for democracy, 243
Child, Prof. C. M., biologist, quoted, 281ff.

317

Epistemology, 48, 110ff.; summarized, 65
Erg-second, in quantum theory, 99
Ethics, in relation to history, 219 *et seq.*
Evolution, formula of, 139; interpretation of, 295; conservative and radical forces in, 295
Evolution, social, its resemblance to chemical autocatalysis, 297; best speed of, 299
Eye, evolution and functions, 86 *et seq.;* in different organisms, 88; visual fields of (chart), 90; vertebrate and invertebrate, 201

F

Fechner, his theory of plant-souls, 36. *See also* Bose
Feuerbach, his materialism, 221
Fisher, Emil, his acid synthesis, 167
Frazer, Sir James, on primitive ethics, 209
Freudian psychology, attitude towards religion and art, 11; on compensation thinking, 11; on reality thinking, 12; psychoanalysis, 31
Freundlich, H., 165
Function, its determination by structure questioned, 124
Functional relationships, in Nature, 127

G

Geocentrism, 25
Geotropism, 215
Gestalt, an emergent whole, 270; theory, 133, 139 *et seq.,* 181ff.; psychology, 237, 265
Gestalten, principles of cultural, 285, 286; social, 279ff.
Greeks, ancient, their rites of sun-worship, 203; development into art of tragedy, 203
Grotthus law, in photochemistry, 159
Growth, as a non-relative motion, 29, 30
Gurwitch, his theory of "mitogenetic" rays, 93

H

Haeckel, E., 23; biogenetic law of, 289
Haldane, J. B. S., 6, 120; his "subjective" theory of color, 103, 104
Hardy, W. G., chemist, 153
Harkins, W. D., chemist, 156
Harvey, Newton, on the oxidization of luciferin, 165
Healy, on circular reaction arcs, 287
Hecht, Selig, on the light-reaction of the eye, 159
Hegel, 61, 219ff.; on change and evolution, 64
Heisenberg, his principle of indeterminacy, x, 118
Helmholtz, his confusion of force and energy, 250
Herrick, C. J., on neurones, 43
History, in relation to ethics, 219 *et seq.*
Hoagland, Hudson, xiv, 215; on redox-potentials, 161
Hobbes, Thos., his theory of thought, 268
Humanism, social objectives of, 304 *et seq.;* its benefit to progress, 309ff.; definition and constituent elements of, 310, 311; its part in social reform, 312; its objectives in detail, 313ff.
Humphrey, Geo., 133

I

Idealism, 4; dynamic, 19; thesis of, 111; strength and weakness of, 111, 112; its theory of one spiritual reality, 268
Individual and social groups, 284
Inertia, 264
Intelligence and morality, close relation of, 308
Interaction. 260
Interfacial forces, 150, 152
Isomorphism, importance of, 177ff.; 186
Isotopes, 260

J

Jaensch, E. R., 209; on eidetic psychology, 104